The M1 does <u>MY</u> talking!

The U.S. M1 Garand Rifle in Pictures
World War Two and the Korean War
Also Origin, Development and Postwar Experimentation
From World War One to the M14

Compiled by Robert Bruce

Revision and Second Printing June 1993
Published in The United States of America by
ROBERT BRUCE PHOTOGRAPHY

P.O. Box 482, Sandston, Virginia 23150 First Printing January, 1992
Copyright 1992-93 by Robert Bruce

Library of Congress Catalog Number 91-90755
International Standard Book Number 0-9631495-1-2

The title of this book is borrowed from artist Jes Schlaikjer's 1945 poster. He, in turn, seems to have borrowed the words from John C. Garand himself. By all accounts a quiet and modest man, Garand did not enjoy the spotlight of wartime publicity. Pressed by a reporter to comment on his monumental contributions to the war effort, he is said to have replied, "My gun speaks loud enough for both of us." Indeed it did, in every corner of the world.

The M-1 does <u>MY</u> talking!

Are you CAREFUL what YOU say or write?

rinted in Hampton, VA by Multi-Print, Inc.

CONTENTS – Present Arms!

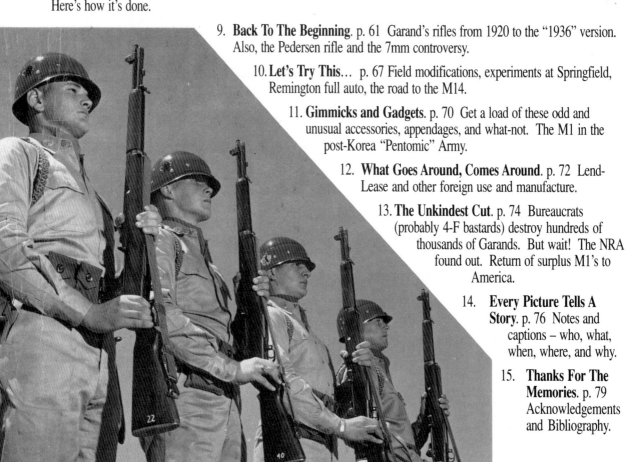

John C. Garand in 1938,
Springfield Armory's Chief Civilian Engineer

Introduction

Archive photographs are much more than documentary history. For in the wink of a shutter so long ago, each has frozen reality on tiny grains of silver. To pause and *really look* at old pictures is to travel back in time. They allow us to peer through a window and connect with people at that very moment in their lives. For those with any imagination at all, the power of the experience can be profound. All the more so for pictures of men and nations at war.

The people in this book live in extraordinary times, when the most basic ideas of freedom are under relentless assault. As we begin in 1938, Germany's Nazi legions are threatening all of Europe. Japan's mechanized Samurai are steamrolling the Chinese masses into submission. The USSR is in the iron grip of a ruthless dictator who has enslaved and murdered millions of his own people.

Here in America, our top military leadership is quietly preparing for what they know to be inevitable global war — a mere twenty years since the close of "The war to end all wars." Tanks, artillery, aircraft, and ships will be needed in unprecedented numbers, along with men to crew them. But most basic of all will be the time-honored need for *riflemen* to close with the enemy to take and hold ground. And so the Garand rifle.

Alone among combatants on both sides of history's most monumental war, America's infantrymen will benefit immeasurably from having as standard issue this semiautomatic rifle. Its accuracy, reliability, and high volume of effective fire often gave our GI's the decisive edge in battle. From frozen misery of the Aleutians to steaming South Pacific jungles, from the blowing sands of North Africa through Hitler's "Fortress Europe," the M1 steadily gained the respect and admiration of friend and foe alike.

The story of the M1 rifle has been told in depth and quite well in a number of readily available books. Despite its flaws, the best of the lot is **Hatcher's Book of the Garand**, by the late Major General Julian S. Hatcher. He was, literally, *there* for the entire period of semiauto rifle development by the Army from WW1 through the end of WW2.

The postwar evolution of the M1 into the selective fire M14 is fully detailed in R. Blake Stevens' book **U.S. Rifle M14 from John Garand to the M21.** These two, and several other noteworthy titles, are given here in the bibliography on page 79.

In contrast, *my book* is intended to supplement these excellent reference works by providing as many documentary photographs and other contemporary images as are physically possible to pack into a reasonable number of pages. As such, explanatory text is noticeably absent (see Chapter 14 for notes and captions), and I apologize to those who may have some difficulty following the story as it is presented.

In compensation, I hope that all who view these old pictures will have a better understanding of why the M1 is much more than just an outstanding battle rifle. Carried at one time or another by most of over 12 million American servicemen and women who served faithfully in WW2 and Korea, I strongly feel it represents the inventive genius, industrial might, and national resolve of the greatest nation on earth. This, at a time when the future of freedom itself was in gravest peril.

Over the past five years or so, a few days at a time here and there, I have been afforded the privilege of combing the picture collections at the National Archives and other official repositories, as well as private holdings.

An infinitesimally small number of these priceless images from America's military past are presented here, but I have chosen thoughtfully and with great care. Historians, collectors, and shooters will find much to study and learn in over 300 photos, drawings, paintings, and posters.

But GI's will find even more. This is YOUR rifle, the way you will remember just like it was yesterday.

So, put on a Glenn Miller record and settle back in an easy chair for a trip down memory lane...

3

1 THE RIFLEMAN'S NEW WEAPON

By 1938, the Army had been exhaustively testing Garand's .30 caliber gas-operated semiautomatic rifles for about ten years. In the lab, on the range, and in the hands of real troops, problems encountered at each stage had been corrected under Garand's personal direction by Springfield Armory craftsmen. This had led to standardization on January 9th, 1936 of the "Rifle, Semiautomatic, M1", and some 2000 production line M1's were delivered in the next two years. But these first production rifles were having a few more teething problems than are revealed in the following article, and wild rumors were bouncing around the Army. In response, the Chief of Ordnance encouraged knowledgeable officers to prepare information articles for professional publications like *ARMY ORDNANCE* and *INFANTRY JOURNAL*, as well as the highly influential civilian monthly *AMERICAN RIFLEMAN*.

From *INFANTRY JOURNAL*, Sep-Oct 1938.
©1938 US Army Infantry Association.
Reproduced by permission of the
Association of the US Army.

The Rifleman's New Weapon

The new semiautomatic rifle, soon to become familiar to certain units, has made good in a big way. Numerous tests by the Infantry Board of U. S. Rifle, Caliber .30, M-1, and the firing conducted by the Regular Class of The Infantry School, have more than justified the expectations instilled by performances of experimental models.

The new weapon has received a thorough workout. Results indicate that men armed with it not only will fire much more rapidly than with the 1903 rifle, but more accurately and with less fatigue, and that they can maintain accuracy during a far longer period. The tests have shown, too, that the new weapon is staunch mechanically, and that malfunctions can be expected to be few.

Soon after this article appears, approximately 7,500 of the new M-1 rifles should have traveled from the production line to the hands of troops. The future of the weapon will then rest largely in the hands of line officers. Extended tests indicate that if they apply the simple regulations governing mechanical training, care, and use, the M-1 rifle will realize a fire power at least two and a half times greater than the Springfield. Indeed, Benning tests show that the average soldier is capable of attaining a sustained cadence of fire of 30 shots a minute with the M-1 rifle and, moreover, that it is comparatively easy to train him to fire with satisfactory efficiency. Among the recent tests by the Department of Experiment is one that offers an interesting comparison between the two rifles.

In this test, two groups of ten recruits (and just to make it harder, Field Artillery recruits at that) who had never fired a rifle, were turned over to two officers of less than

"Load"

one year's service. The first group was armed with the Springfield, the second with the M-1 rifle. Each group was given 3½ days training in nomenclature, assembly, and disassembly, care and cleaning, service of the rifle, functioning, immediate action and stoppages, and preparatory marksmanship. Each group then fired at 1,000 inches on the same type of target, approximately the same number of rounds per man, and on the following day fired at 200, 300, and 500 yards. The per cent of hits on the 1,000-inch range was 66% for the Springfield group and 87% for the M-1 group. At the longer ranges the results were 80% for the Springfield group and 91% for the M-1 group.

Then, on the following day, each group fired a combat problem involving firing for a minute and twenty seconds, at each of three ranges—200, 300, and 500 yards—a total firing time of four minutes. The Springfield group fired 364 rounds and made 246 hits (67%), an average of 6.1 hits per minute per man. The M-1 group fired 689 rounds and made 576 hits (83%), an average of 14.4 hits per minute per man.

The superior accuracy of men armed with the M-1 was not an isolated example. In the opinion of the Department of Experiment, men armed with the M-1 and given the same amount of preliminary training as men armed with the Springfield, will consistently outshoot them. Moreover, with considerably less training they will shoot fully as well as men armed with the older weapon. It is true that more time is required for mechanical training with the M-1 rifle. But less time is needed for preliminary marksmanship training which can be immediately concentrated on essentials, such as sighting, aiming, position, trigger squeeze, and time fire.

The outstanding factor, however, is the fact that the much lighter recoil does not hurt the inexperienced firer the first time he fires a shot, hence the tendency to flinch is markedly less. On the other hand, a man firing the 1903 rifle for the first time often does not hold the rifle tightly and consequently gets smacked on the jaw. Or his thumb strikes his nose or a finger digs into his face. Gone

"Aim"

ORD 13078

6

then are the lessons previously learned. The man concentrates on protecting himself from the kick of the rifle, and flinching is the result. In fact, the emphasis on trigger squeeze is largely based on combating this inherent fear of the recoil. Because of the far lighter recoil of the M-1 rifle, this fear is eliminated in nearly all cases. The firer can concentrate his entire attention on correct aiming and getting the shot off while his aim is correct without disturbing his aim. His trigger squeeze can be very fast and still not disturb his aim, for very few men have a tendency to flinch with the M-1, and jerk the trigger.

Another thing which increases accuracy and reduces training time is the sight of the M-1. The big, broad front sight never blurs, the rear peep is close to the eye, and the elevation drum on the rear sight can be zeroed and set in such a manner that if the soldier wishes to fire at a range of 300 yards he sets 300 yards on his sight. He does not have to remember that at 300 yards it is necessary to set 340 (and there isn't any 40-yard graduation). Furthermore, elevation and deflection changes are in minutes of angle, and each of the clicks will move a bullet one inch for each hundred yards of range both in elevation and deflection. One simple problem illustrated on a target will be enough for a group of men. No longer will they be bothered with using complicated tables for points of windage.

Another important characteristic of the M-1 rifle and one which greatly increases its value in combat, in the opinion of the Department of Experiment, is the huge saving in fatigue of the firer. A test was conducted with three groups of twenty men each, one armed with the M-1 rifle, one with the Springfield, and one with the M-1922 caliber .22 rifle. After sixty consecutive shots the efficiency of the fire of the men armed with the Springfield began to fall off rapidly; after 150 consecutive shots the men were merely seeking to get the ordeal over; and after 300 consecutive shots none of them were capable of firing. On the next day when it was planned to repeat the test, the men said they were unable to do so and would rather go to the hospital than fire any more with the Springfield. The men of the group firing the M-1922 caliber .22 rifles were in almost as bad a condition after 300 rounds. Although no faces had been battered, the continual turning of the butt plate during the manipulation of the bolt had made their shoulders actually raw. These men were willing to fire the next day but said their shoulders were so stiff they did not think they could shoot with any accuracy. The men armed with the M-1 rifles

"Thrust"

ORD13080

The squad leader demonstrates field stripping.

fired their 300 shots at a steady rate, and there was no complaining. Accuracy decreased somewhat after 150 rounds because their left arms became tired. But even beyond 300 rounds their accuracy was still good enough for all normal combat firing. On the following day all these men were willing to fire and did so, and their accuracy and rate of fire was about the same as on the previous day. A few men said that their left arms were a bit stiff from tight slings, but otherwise they had suffered no ill effects. As a further test, one man fired 700 consecutive rounds at a rate of about twenty-five rounds a minute. He wore no shirt, the butt plate resting against his bare shoulder. No ill effects were visible except that the checkering of the butt plate "pinked" his skin slightly.

Test firing indicates that a properly lubricated M-1 rifle using suitable ammunition should not develop any malfunctions until about 400 rounds have been fired. However, careful lubrication is essential. Under normal conditions about 98% of the malfunctions will result from a breakdown in the lubrication of the weapon. The exact point at which this will occur will depend largely upon the care with which the weapon is lubricated and the rate of fire to which it is subjected.

In one test 300 consecutive shots were fired with each of ten rifles in about 15 minutes without any malfunctions occurring. One rifle fired 527 rounds in approximately

Rear view of the M-1 rifle showing 8-round cartridge clip.

Kneeling position.

21 minutes and then a failure to feed occurred. Another rifle was fired 328 rounds in about 7 minutes. No malfunctions occurred, but the rate of fire was so great that the forearm began to char. This last was not aimed fire.

It should be understood that malfunctions occurring from lack of lubrication do not place the rifle out of action until more lubrication can be applied. The firer can still operate the rifle by pulling back the operating rod for each shot. Actually, a greater rate of fire can be delivered with the M-1 rifle in this manner than with the 1903 rifle, probably because it is easier to operate, even in that manner, and because the 8-round clip requires fewer reloadings. So far as known, the only malfunctions that will render the weapon unserviceable are those resulting from the breakage of an essential part.

The experience of the Department of Experiment has been that the M-1 rifles, like new automobiles, are a bit stiff and inclined to be sluggish at first. After they have been fired some, the small imperfections in metal surfaces

in contact become polished and smooth. The more the rifles are fired, provided they are kept properly lubricated, the easier the action becomes and the greater the number of rounds that can be fired without malfunction.

The Regular Class at The Infantry School fired with ninety-eight M-1 rifles and thirty-three old experimental rifles borrowed from the 29th Infantry. The M-1 rifles had far fewer malfunctions. After a short period of preliminary training and four hours of instruction practice at 200 yards, the students recorded scores as follows:

4 rounds, kneeling, slow fire
16 rounds, prone to prone, 25-yard rush (60 seconds)
8 rounds, prone to kneeling, 25-yard rush (27 seconds)

The high individual score was 139 out of a possible 140, and the average score was 109.9. Of the 143 students firing, nine scored 130 or higher.

Thus, on all counts, the M-1 rifle appears to be a great advance in the basic shoulder weapon of the infantry soldier.

AUGUST 1938

THE AMERICAN RIFLEMAN

25 CENTS

John Garand, age 50, poses with his "1936" first production model M1. With hunting and target shooting a passion for millions of red-blooded American men, the influence of the National Rifle Association's *AMERICAN RIFLEMAN* magazine was not to be doubted. Closely attuned with the military through the Director of Civilian Marksmanship (DCM) programs, the NRA also counted a high percentage of current and former servicemen among its membership. It must have been with much appreciation at the office of the Chief of Ordnance that Major G.H. Drewry's article, "Our New Service Rifle", was accepted for publication in the August '38 *RIFLEMAN*. Essentially the same in content as the *INFANTRY JOURNAL* feature, it included these excellent line drawings, thoughtfully provided by the Ordnance Department.

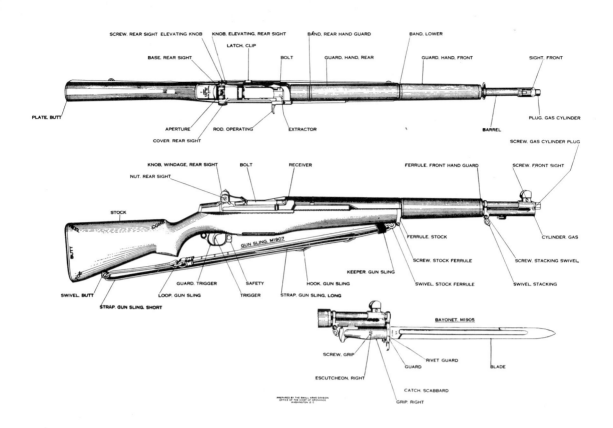

SCREW. REAR SIGHT ELEVATING KNOB
KNOB, ELEVATING, REAR SIGHT
BAND, REAR HAND GUARD
BAND, LOWER
LATCH, CLIP
BASE, REAR SIGHT
BOLT
GUARD, HAND, REAR
GUARD, HAND, FRONT
SIGHT, FRONT
PLATE. BUTT
APERTURE
ROD, OPERATING
EXTRACTOR
COVER. REAR SIGHT
BARREL
PLUG. GAS CYLINDER
SCREW. GAS CYLINDER PLUG

KNOB, WINDAGE, REAR SIGHT
BOLT
RECEIVER
FERRULE, FRONT HAND GUARD
SCREW. FRONT SIGHT
NUT. REAR SIGHT
STOCK
FERRULE, STOCK
CYLINDER. GAS
SCREW. STOCK FERRULE
SCREW. STACKING SWIVEL,
GUN SLING, M1907
KEEPER. GUN SLING
SWIVEL. STACKING
SWIVEL. BUTT
GUARD, TRIGGER
SAFETY
HOOK. GUN SLING
SWIVEL. STOCK FERRULE
LOOP, GUN SLING
TRIGGER
STRAP. GUN SLING, LONG
STRAP. GUN SLING, SHORT

BAYONET. M1905
SCREW, GRIP
RIVET GUARD
GUARD
BLADE
ESCUTCHEON, RIGHT
CATCH. SCABBARD
GRIP. RIGHT

PREPARED BY THE SMALL ARMS DIVISION
OFFICE OF THE CHIEF OF ORDNANCE
WASHINGTON D C.

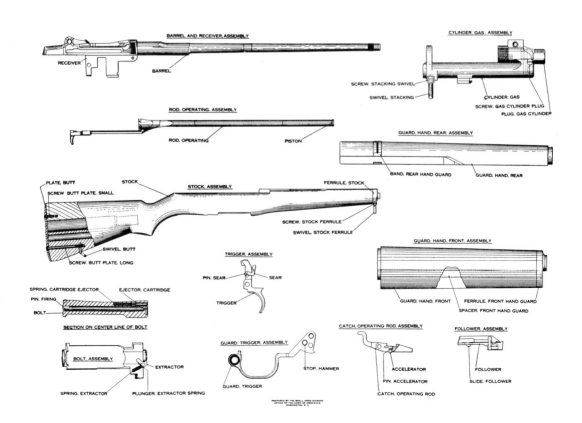

BARREL AND RECEIVER, ASSEMBLY
RECEIVER
BARREL
CYLINDER, GAS. ASSEMBLY
SCREW. STACKING SWIVEL
SWIVEL. STACKING
CYLINDER. GAS
SCREW. GAS CYLINDER PLUG
PLUG. GAS CYLINDER

ROD, OPERATING. ASSEMBLY
ROD, OPERATING
PISTON
GUARD, HAND, REAR. ASSEMBLY
BAND, REAR HAND GUARD
GUARD, HAND, REAR

PLATE. BUTT
STOCK
STOCK. ASSEMBLY
FERRULE. STOCK
SCREW. BUTT PLATE. SMALL
SCREW. STOCK FERRULE
SWIVEL. STOCK FERRULE
SWIVEL. BUTT
SCREW. BUTT PLATE. LONG

GUARD, HAND, FRONT. ASSEMBLY
SPRING. CARTRIDGE EJECTOR
EJECTOR. CARTRIDGE
TRIGGER. ASSEMBLY
PIN. FIRING
PIN. SEAR
SEAR
GUARD, HAND, FRONT
FERRULE, FRONT HAND GUARD
BOLT
TRIGGER
SPACER. FRONT HAND GUARD

SECTION ON CENTER LINE OF BOLT
CATCH. OPERATING ROD. ASSEMBLY
FOLLOWER. ASSEMBLY
BOLT, ASSEMBLY
EXTRACTOR
GUARD, TRIGGER. ASSEMBLY
STOP. HAMMER
ACCELERATOR
FOLLOWER
SPRING. EXTRACTOR
PLUNGER, EXTRACTOR SPRING
GUARD. TRIGGER
PIN. ACCELERATOR
SLIDE. FOLLOWER
CATCH. OPERATING ROD

PREPARED BY THE SMALL ARMS DIVISION
OFFICE OF THE CHIEF OF ORDNANCE
WASHINGTON D C.

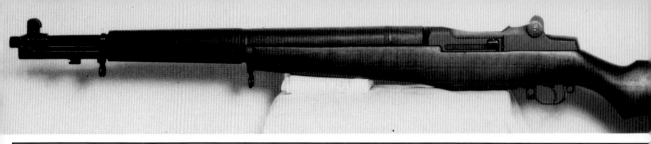

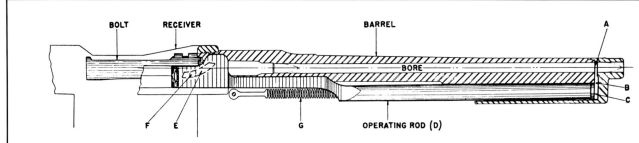

The "1936" M1's principle of operation is clearly presented in the diagram above, showing how propellant gas is diverted at the muzzle (A) and enters the gas cylinder (B). There, it expands and moves the piston C) and operating rod (D) rearward. A cam cut (E) moves the bolt lug (F) to unlock the bolt from the receiver, extracting and ejecting the spent cartridge. The operating rod spring (G) compressed by rearward movement of the action, expands to drive the bolt forward, feeding, chambering, and locking a fresh round.

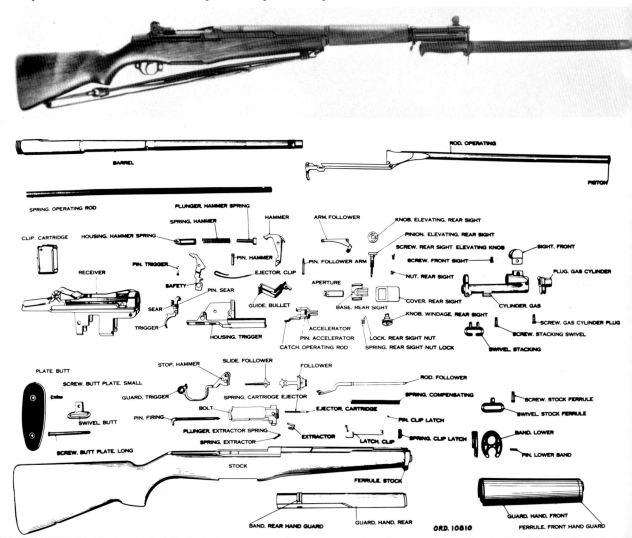

THE OLD AND THE NEW

Look closely here, because initial appearances can be deceptive. At the top,
doughboys in the Philippines in 1941 wearing old style campaign hats are armed
with the new "1940" version M1, characterized by a redesigned gas cylinder. Below
them, soldiers at Ft. Benning in August '41 model the new M1 helmet, but are armed
with "1936" version rifles. Note the horse cavalryman at the top of the page with
his Garand in a scabbard and new "steel pot" attached to his McClellan saddle.

2 1000 GARANDS A DAY

At the rate of about ten per day, the first production model M1's began coming off the antiquated line at Springfield Armory in September, 1937. Gradually, as new machinery and techniques came into use, output rose to 200 a day by January 1940, and then 1000 a day by mid-1941. At the same time over at Winchester – which had been given a $1,380,000 "educational order" in 1939 to prepare for M1 rifle production – they were building 100 a day on their 65,000 rifle contract. Employees at both locations were working shifts around the clock, and we weren't even at war. Not yet.

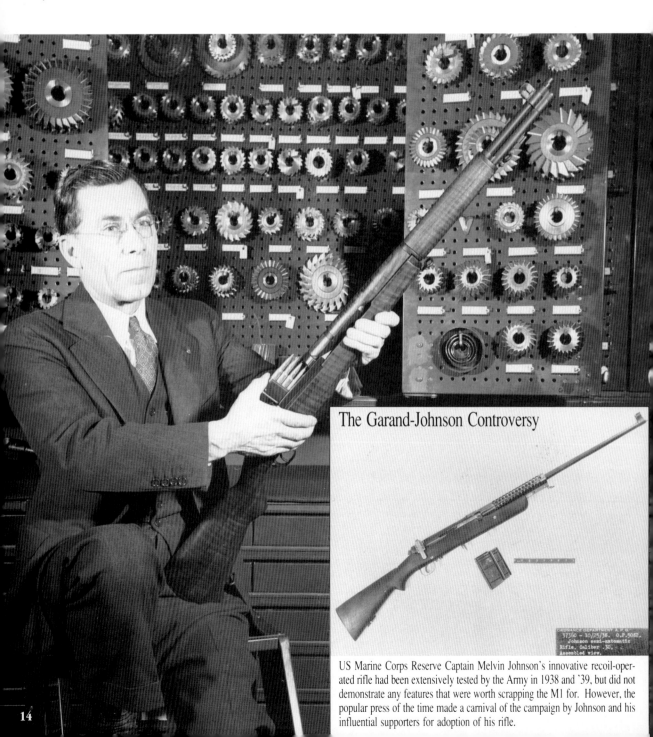

The Garand-Johnson Controversy

US Marine Corps Reserve Captain Melvin Johnson's innovative recoil-operated rifle had been extensively tested by the Army in 1938 and '39, but did not demonstrate any features that were worth scrapping the M1 for. However, the popular press of the time made a carnival of the campaign by Johnson and his influential supporters for adoption of his rifle.

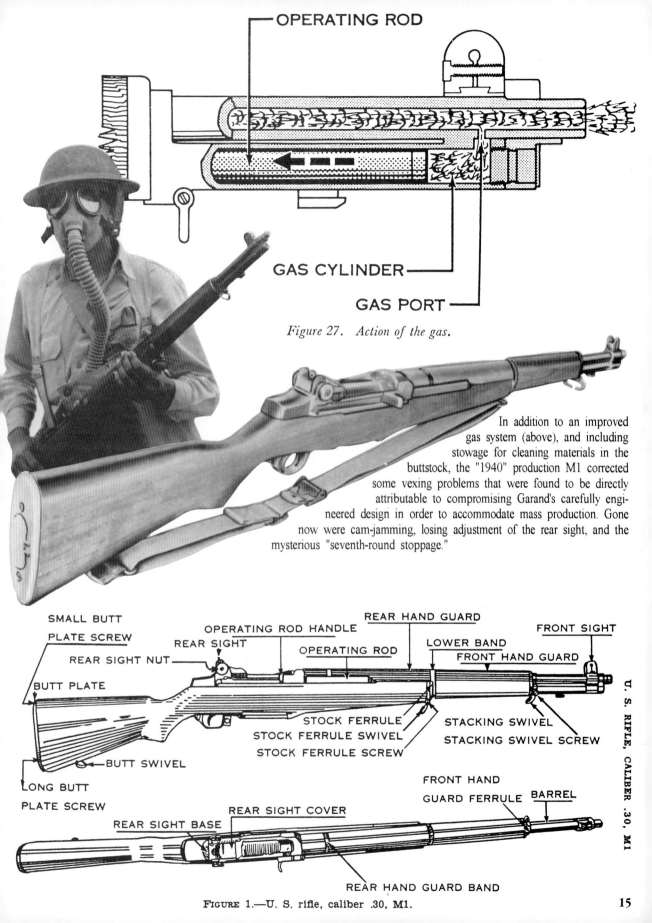

OPERATING ROD

GAS CYLINDER

GAS PORT

Figure 27. Action of the gas.

In addition to an improved gas system (above), and including stowage for cleaning materials in the buttstock, the "1940" production M1 corrected some vexing problems that were found to be directly attributable to compromising Garand's carefully engineered design in order to accommodate mass production. Gone now were cam-jamming, losing adjustment of the rear sight, and the mysterious "seventh-round stoppage."

SMALL BUTT
PLATE SCREW

REAR SIGHT NUT

BUTT PLATE

OPERATING ROD HANDLE

REAR SIGHT

REAR HAND GUARD

OPERATING ROD

LOWER BAND

FRONT SIGHT

FRONT HAND GUARD

STOCK FERRULE

STOCK FERRULE SWIVEL

STOCK FERRULE SCREW

STACKING SWIVEL

STACKING SWIVEL SCREW

BUTT SWIVEL

LONG BUTT
PLATE SCREW

REAR SIGHT BASE

REAR SIGHT COVER

FRONT HAND
GUARD FERRULE

BARREL

REAR HAND GUARD BAND

FIGURE 1.—U. S. rifle, caliber .30, M1.

"Give 'em the stuff to fight with..."

JOHN FALTER 42

WORK FOR FREEDOM !

In the fall of 1941 Springfield Armory's production of 1000 Garands per day looked good, but after Pearl Harbor it fell far short of meeting requirements. It had to be raised to 2,000 per day, and then boosted to 3,000 while Winchester raised its output from 100 to 750 per day.

Although having fewer parts than the '03 Springfield, the Garand was still not a snap to make. Almost a thousand machining operations went into its seventy some components.

The battle begins with your job! DO IT RIGHT

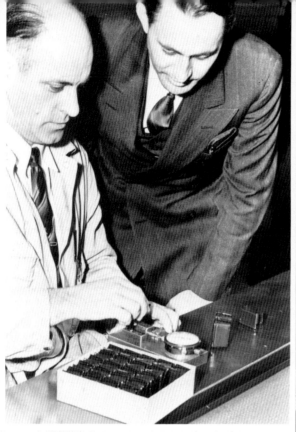

WARNER & SWASEY'S ARE WEAPONS — *MAKE THE MOST OF TH*

4436-SA   SPRINGFIELD ARMORY · ORDNANCE DEPT. 18 March 44
CLIP, U.S. Rifle Cal.30 M1 Loaded - Unloaded

At the top of the facing page a Woman Ordnance Worker (W.O.W.) fron Springfield tries out a Garand fresh off the production line. While jus below her, a brand new GI receives an equally new M1 as the suppl sergeant carefully records its serial number. Hard times were ahead fc both the recruit and his rifle.

"In August 1942, total production amounted to 68,660 for the month while requirements to the end of the program in June 1944 stood at about four million, or 200,000 per month. It was a huge gap that was not closed until the war was nearly over." **(US Army in WW2, The Technical Services, The Ordnance Department: Procurement and Supply)**

WHOSE BOY WILL DIE
IF WE SHOULD FAIL?

SUPPLY SERGEANT

3 "THE M1 RIFLE IS THE GREATEST BATTLE IMPLEMENT EVEF

—— Lt. Gen. George S. Patton, Jr. 26 January 1945 ——

"US troops entered World War II with semiautomatic rifles that gave them a decided advantage over their enemies. No other major power equipped its soldiers with a really good semiautomatic rifle. The Russians used the M1940 Tokarev rifle extensively but abandoned it because of its many inherent defects. During the war the Germans produced a few semiautomatics but

DEVISED"

Patton, it is said, was not one to give excessive praise. This makes it all the more remarkable that a horse cavalryman turned tanker would write so highly of the Garand in a letter to the Chief of Ordnance.

they were never very effective and did not reach the battlefield in significant numbers. The standard German rifle at the end of the war was still a bolt-action piece. The only reasonably satisfactory Japanese semiautomatic in World War II was an imitation of the Garand." (**US Army in WW2, The Technical Services, The Ordnance Department: Procurement and Supply**)

Despite the stated bias of this book, the M1 was not the only infantry weapon in the inventory at the outbreak of war. As can be seen from this photo above, a display on Guadalcanal in October, '43, soldiers and marines had a wide variety, suitable for many different jobs.

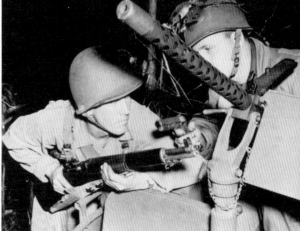

But the M1 was the basic killing tool, used throughout the Pacific Theater. It is a tribute to the man and his weapon that the Garand worked so well in those dank, steaming jungles where rain, mud, rust, and fungus sometimes rivaled the Japs as an enemy.

MILES OF HELL
to Tokyo!

WORK WHERE
YOU'RE NEEDED

CONSULT YOUR U.S. EMPLOYMENT SERVICE OFFICE
WAR MANPOWER COMMISSION

We'll lick 'em—
JUST GIVE US THE METAL!

③ Parts disassembled.

FIGURE 4.—Rear sight, U. S. rifle, caliber .30, M1.

U.S. ARMY FIELD RATION K
DINNER UNIT

COVER

MODIFIED PINION

MODIFIED NUT

SCREW

KNOB

PINION

BASE

KNOB

SPRING
AND
NUT
LOCK

NUT

APERTURE

Joe, Army Sergeant Bill Mauldin's archetypical GI and inseparable buddy of Willie, eloquently speaks for a whole generation of young men who carried the M1 during WW2. This, along with over 400 more of Mauldin's best wartime cartoons, can be found in **Bill Mauldin's Army**, published by Presidio Press. Used by permission of Bill Mauldin. Thanks!

"I've given you th' best years o' my life."

FIGURE 32.—Sight picture, U. S. rifle, caliber .30,

LEADS
(MAN WALKING)

100 YARDS
200 YARDS
300 YARDS
400 YARDS
500 YARDS
WIDTH OF BODY

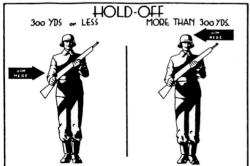

HOLD-OFF

300 YDS or LESS   MORE THAN 300 YDS.

AIM HERE   AIM HERE

The Russians wanted to know how good the American rifle was; so Pfc. Elijah Sams and Pvt. Eldon Ramsey helped a Red infantryman try out our M-I.

CONTINENTAL EDITION

YANK
THE ARMY WEEKLY

3 FRANCS

MAY 6
1945
VOL. 1, NO. 41

By the men...for the
men in the service

KOREA 1950 - 53

"By its participation in the Korean conflict the Army of the United States, in a determined effort to restore international peace and security, has been for the first time committed to battle under the flag of the United Nations. Confronted by the most arduous conditions, the American soldier has fought with traditional bravery and skill against communist aggression in Korea. He has met every test with honor." J. Lawton Collins, Chief of Staff of the Army (Foreword to **Korea 1950**)

Barely five years after VJ Day, US riflemen were firing shots in anger once again. As fast as the clinging Cosmoline could be removed and WW2 production ammo uncrated, the M1 was back in business in a big way.

As it had in WW2, the Garand performed admirably under the "most arduous conditions". In his respected analysis of infantry weapons and small unit actions in Korea, Brigadier General S.L.A. Marshall wrote of the M1: "The issue rifle has performed adequately in Korea and is regarded by troops with a liking amounting to affection. This is true of all forces, Army and Marines alike. They have found that it stands up ruggedly against the most extreme tests by terrain, weather, and rough handling. They want the weapon left as it is now, and they have no suggestions as to how it might be changed for the better."

The Leathernecks are telling the Axis with bullets

AGAIN the hard-hitting U. S. Marines are living up to their great fighting tradition—telling it to the Axis in the only language our enemies understand, the language of bullets.

Many members of the Army, Navy and Marines were already good shots before entering the service—trained with accurate Western Super-Match and Xpert cartridges on the ranges of hun-dreds of civilian rifle clubs throughout the country, and at the great national rifle matches at Camp Perry, Ohio.

Now, millions of Western military cartridges are going to the men of our armed forces — backing them up in battle, just as the World Champion Ammunition helped to improve their marksmanship during peace.

Rifles in the illustration are the famous Garands that are being produced in quantity by Winchester.

MORE MARKSMEN FOR AMERICA

Western
CARTRIDGE COMPANY
EAST ALTON, ILLINOIS

SUPER-MATCH
MARK II
SUPER-MATCH
MARK II
.22 Long Rifle Cartridges

4 TELL THAT TO THE MARINES!

Every Marine is, first, foremost, and always, a rifleman. This is perhaps the most basic and unshakable tenet of the Corps.

No matter what job he goes on to perform after the rite of passage that is Marine Boot Camp, he will always be prepared to take up his rifle against the enemy at a moment's notice. Always.

The process by which this has been so successfully done for so long is a science, an art, and virtually a religion in the Corps. The trainee – "Boot" – is not just issued a rifle; he is almost ceremoniously presented with it. Over the next several all-too-long weeks he will come to know it inside and out, to safeguard and care for it, and to shoot it with astounding effectiveness.

The most stirring creed of this warrior religion was written by Marine Major General William Rupertus and widely circulated during WW2. It cannot be improved upon.

American Rifleman
January 1944 p. 3
Used by Permission
.F. Mossberg & Sons, Inc.

"MY RIFLE"

The Creed of a United States Marine

By Major General William H. Rupertus, U.S.M.C.

THIS is my rifle. There are many like it, but this one is mine. ➤ My rifle is my best friend. It is my life. I must master it as I must master my life. ➤ My rifle, without me is useless. Without my rifle, I am useless. I must fire my rifle true. I must shoot straighter than my enemy who is trying to kill me. I must shoot him before he shoots me. I will . . . ➤ My rifle and myself know that what counts in this war is not the rounds we fire, the noise of our burst, nor the smoke we make. We know that it is the hits that count. We will hit . . . ➤ My rifle is human, even as I, because it is my life. Thus, I will learn it as a brother. I will learn its weaknesses, its strength, its parts, its accessories, its sights, and its barrel. I will ever guard it against the ravages of weather and damage as I will ever guard my legs, my arms, my eyes, and my heart against damage. I will keep my rifle clean and ready, even as I am clean and ready. We will become part of each other. We will . . . ➤ Before God I swear this creed. My rifle and myself are the defenders of my country. We are the masters of our enemy. We are the saviors of my life. ➤ So be it, until victory is America's and there is no enemy, but Peace!

I must fire my rifle true.

The vestments and trappings of the cult of the Marine rifleman are eminently practical. Among them are the padded and reinforced shooting jacket with its special pocket for the holy record book, the sling by which tranquility of aim may be attained, and the carbide lamp to induce somber tones to the sights.

(Above) 16 Apr 54, Ft. Benning, GA. Marine marksman Corporal K.R. Twigg shoots while Staff Sergeant Thomas Gilland scores in competition with the Army.

(Below) March 1943, Camp Lejune, NC. Instructing a negro recruit of the 51st Composite Battalion. Office of War Information photo.

After much training and reinforcement the rifle has truly become a part of him, to the point where he will feel incomplete without it. This is how it must be, for the real test of faith lies ahead.

I must shoot him before he shoots me.

ISLAND HOPPING
IN THE
SOUTH PACIFIC

We are the masters of our enemy.

Iwo Jima

our METAL is on the attack
KEEP IT COMING!

I'll give 'em HELL!

YOU GIVE ME THE STUFF!

LET'S GO!

U·S·MARINES

THE ARTIST'S BRUSH IS ALSO A WEAPON

"Good" propaganda was a powerful tool in the job of winning America's hearts and minds. Those on the home front were urged to join, to conserve, to buy, to produce, to support, and sometimes to shut up.

The Gun that sprang from nowhere

SOMEWHERE this minute, as you read this, an enemy of America is looking into the barrel of a gun from nowhere.

A miracle gun, if you please, that would still be a useless hunk of unshaped steel waiting to be machined—except for a discovery of scientists in a United States Steel laboratory.

What was the discovery? The secret of making two gun barrels in the same time it takes to make one.

Imagine what this means. Arms are flowing to our soldiers in constantly increasing quantities. One factory, for example, reports that it will make two years' output of gun barrels in one year!

And as if that weren't dramatic enough, these same men of steel have accomplished a similar miracle in the art of bomb making. Shaping bombs while still white hot metal. Finishing the bomb casing in minutes instead of hours.

Steel landing fields have been invented to cut the time of making an airport to mere hours! Helmets for America's soldiers that stop a .45 automatic bullet . . . Tanks of tougher steels . . . Ways to make machine gun bullets faster than ever before.

What you can expect after the war

The world we live in will be years ahead of itself because of new war-born steel inventions. No other material rivals steel's useful qualities.

U·S·S steels have gone to war in tanks, in planes, in ships, in bullets. They'll be back better than ever. You'll find these U·S·S trade-marked steels building a new and greater America in the peace years to come.

AMERICAN BRIDGE COMPANY · AMERICAN STEEL & WIRE COMPANY · BOYLE MANUFACTURING COMPANY · CARNEGIE-ILLINOIS STEEL CORPORATION · COLUMBIA STEEL COMPANY · CYCLONE FENCE DIVISION · FEDERAL SHIPBUILDING & DRY DOCK COMPANY · NATIONAL TUBE COMPANY · OIL WELL SUPPLY COMPANY · TENNESSEE COAL, IRON & RAILROAD COMPANY · TUBULAR ALLOY STEEL CORPORATION · UNITED STATES STEEL EXPORT COMPANY · UNITED STATES STEEL SUPPLY COMPANY · UNIVERSAL ATLAS CEMENT COMPANY · VIRGINIA BRIDGE COMPANY

NEW STEELS FOR AMERICA

USS STEELS

UNITED STATES STEEL

* BUY WAR BONDS EVERY PAYDAY

The money you loan builds America's war strength. Yours again to spend in years to come . . . for new comforts, products of steel, things for better living.

Magazine, 1 March 1943. Used by permission of USX Corp.

Painted with the coperation of the U. S. Marine Corps.

SEMPER FIDELIS

NOVEMBER 10 1775 - 1943

168th ANNIVERSARY

U.S.MARINE CORPS

ATTACK ATTACK ATTACK

Y WAR BONDS

CARELESS TALK Got there First

Help him get through!

BUY WAR BONDS

We're on our Way!

The Navy moves in on a sea of Oil

Stick to your Job...Oil is Ammunition

REAL ART.

You know it when you see it. No time for abstracts or impressionism – give us heroic realism anytime. Too bad we don't see this stuff anymore.

Many of America's most talented artists pitched in at the studio, and sometimes at the battlefront.

LET'S **ALL** FIGHT

BUY WAR BONDS

YOU'VE GOT WHAT IT TAKES, SOLDIER—

NOW TAKE CARE OF WHAT YOU'VE GOT!

DESIGNED FOR LIVING

TAKE CARE OF YOUR **GAS MASK**
DON'T USE IT AS A KNAPSACK OR PILLOW

SOLDIER—
TAKE CARE OF YOUR **G.I.**

—AND IT WILL TAKE CARE —OF YOU

AMERICA HAS PLENTY IF *IT IS USED WISELY!*

Don't waste precious materiel

Your RED CROSS is at his side

LIKE DIGGING A FOXHOLE

It's for your own protection

MAKE CONSERVATION A HABIT

silence—

—means security
BE CAREFUL WHAT YOU SAY OR WRITE

A rock to Joe Dope is a trifle
That is promptly pried loose with his rifle..
But when later the sap
Tries to shoot at a Jap
The explosion will be quite an eyeful.!

Don't be a dope.!   **HANDLE EQUIPMENT RIGHT !**

(left) JOE DOPE was created by GI artist Will Eisner. The lesson always came in BURMA-SHAVE type verse.

"To Make Men Free" (right) by beloved artist Norman Rockwell was commissioned by the Army early in the war.

KODACHROMES.

The science of color photography was well advanced during WW2. It's just that we are most accustomed to seeing the black and white images of the time. Relatively few by comparison, these rare color pictures comprise a strong and vivid record of men at arms in WW2 and Korea.

We are the saviors of my life.   Okinawa

Until Victory is   America's...

KOREA

... and there is no enemy, but Peace!

5 "LONG DISTANCE, CALLING!"

The Army has a tradition dating back to the Civil War of mounting telescopic sights on rifles specially selected for accuracy. While we started WW2 with the M1903 Springfield and scope as standard sniper configuration, it wasn't long before experimentation started on the Garand. After all, it was reasoned, many of the characteristics of a semiauto rifle lend themselves quite well to the task. Most prominent of these include a quick second shot capability, and no need for position-disclosing movement to manipulate the bolt for each shot. Problem was, the scope had to be radically offset to allow top loading of clipped ammo.

The Weapon Sight Kit T-1 is the latest in a series of improvements of the heavy, short-range Sniperscope which was first introduced in our Army late in World War II. It operates in the infrared frequencies, which are not visible to the unaided human eye. Included in the kit, which is adaptable to all infantry weapons, is an infrared light source, and a telescope which converts the infrared light to a form which is visible. The entire equipment weighs less than ten pounds, including the infrared light source battery." US Army Infantry Board official photograph, Ft. Benning, GA, 27 Aug 58.

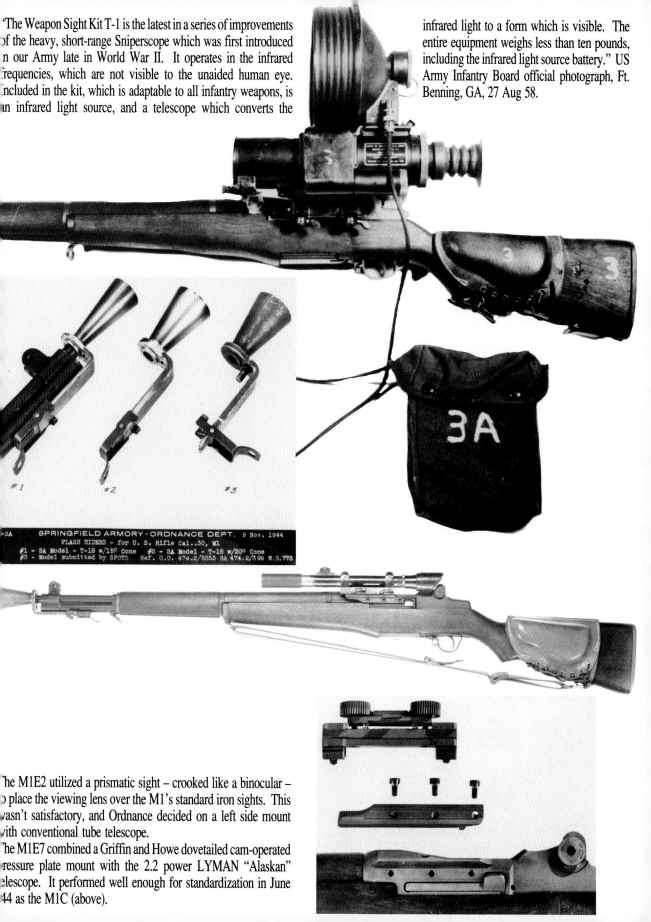

SPRINGFIELD ARMORY - ORDNANCE DEPT. 9 Nov. 1944
FLASH HIDERS - for U. S. Rifle Cal..30, M1
#1 - SA Model - T-18 w/15° Cone   #2 - SA Model - T-18 w/20° Cone
#3 - Model submitted by SPOTS   Ref. O.O. 474.2/5853 SA 474.2/399 W.O.773

The M1E2 utilized a prismatic sight – crooked like a binocular – to place the viewing lens over the M1's standard iron sights. This wasn't satisfactory, and Ordnance decided on a left side mount with conventional tube telescope.

The M1E7 combined a Griffin and Howe dovetailed cam-operated pressure plate mount with the 2.2 power LYMAN "Alaskan" telescope. It performed well enough for standardization in June 44 as the M1C (above).

M84 telescope reticle.

Three months later, the Springfield Armory-designed M1E8 was designated "substitute standard" as the M1D (above). Its M73/M81/M82 scope (all variants of the LYMAN "Alaskan") was mounted by a single hefty screw to a machined block pinned to the chamber end of the barrel. Both the M1C and D were usually issued with the T4 leather cheek pad and M2 flash hider.

Army sniper-spotter teams in Korea. Despite the inadequate power of the issue scope, the M1C and D combinations were tough and usually quite effective well beyond 600 – 800 yards.
(bottom) A Vietnamese Regional Forces sniper sights his M1D.

6 THE SPIRIT OF THE BAYONET!

The real need for bayonets has been hotly debated ever since the advent of metallic cartridges and magazine feed. However, it remains an article of faith among infantry leaders that bayonet training contributes greatly to fighting spirit. And besides, there have been times in modern battle when cold glistening steel has saved the day by boosting morale and gutting bad guys eye-to-eye.

What's the Spirit of the Bayonet? "TO KILL!"

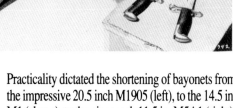

Korea, 30 Mar 51. (above) PFC John Allen of Co. E, 35th Regimental Combat Team, 25th Infantry Division.

Practicality dictated the shortening of bayonets from the impressive 20.5 inch M1905 (left), to the 14.5 in. M1 (above), to the pipsqueak 11.5 in. M5A1 (right). But the M5 could get those C-Rats open in a flash!

7 GRENADIER!

PLATE 66. ANTITANK RIFLE GRENADE M9A1.

PLATE 67. IMPACT FRAG-MENTATION RIFLE GREN-ADE M17 (FORMERLY T2).

PLATE 68. SMOKE RIFLE GRENADE (HC) M20.

The value of rifle-launched grenades was well proven in the trenches of the first World War, and it wasn't long into the second that the Garand was so equipped.

Taken on 4 Dec 43 at Ft. Benning, the picture above identifies Colonel Charles Coates (center) of the Infantry Board as the "inventor of the grenade launcher" for the M1. Ray Miller of the Ordnance Shop at Benning shows how it attaches, while Colonel Myron Leedy looks on. The assortment of rifle grenades on the table included types that had been in the inventory for some time, used with the '03 rifle. All were launched with a special high pressure blank, and many fatalities among GI's came from forgetting in the heat of battle to clear ball ammo from the chamber!

RENADE LAUNCHER M-7... & RELATED PARTS
U. S. RIFLE, CAL. .30, M1

TCH ENGAGES BAYONET LUG

THESE GROOVES PREDETERMINE THE DISTANCES THE FRAGMENTATION GRENADE WILL BE FIRED WHEN HELD AT AN ANGLE OF 45°
For range of various rings see appropriate FM or TM

USE ONLY GRENADE CARTRIDGE (ALWAYS HANDLOAD IN RIFLE)

BODY

GRENADE RETAINER SPRING

NUT

STUD HOLDS VALVE OPEN

LATCH PIVOTS AS SHOWN TO LOCK LAUNCHER TO BAYONET LUG. FORMING AN INTEGRAL PART

GAS CYLINDER VALVE SCREW FURNISHED WITH LAUNCHER
(THIS VALVE SCREW REPLACES REGULAR LOCK SCREW AND IS THEN USED FOR EITHER GRENADE CARTRIDGE OR REGULAR SERVICE AMMUNITION)

ORD. No. 17993

MOUNTING PLATE

① MOUNTING PLATE NOTCHES   CLICK SPRING TIP

②

③

FRONT SIGHT POST

ELEVATING SCREW
1 CLICK EQUALS 12" ELEVATION
5 CLICKS EQUALS 1° ELEVATION

REAR (PEEP) SIGHT

Figure 43. Grenade launcher sight (M15).

8 AWRIGHT... LISSEN UP!

It's my LIFE...
if the TRAINING PROGRAM fails

The American GI learns best when he is taught not only how, but why. Not content with merely learning to strip, clean, and reassemble his rifle, he has to know how the parts work together and why they're made that way. In support of this, a wide variety of training aids were developed to show the maximum number of men in the shortest practical time all the ins and outs of the Garand. These included the giant wooden working model shown below, and the disassembly mat at right. There were also illustrated manuals, lantern and filmstrip slides, movies, flip charts, and the amusing oversized mockup M24.

FIGURE 119.—Working model—M1 rifle.

RIFLE, U.S. ..30, M1

1- TRI... ...SING GROUP
2- STOCK GROUP
3- FOLLOWER ROD AND OPERATING ROD SPRING

4- FOLLOWER ARM PIN
5- BULLET GUIDE
6- FOLLOWER ARM
7- OPERATING ROD CATCH ASSEMBLY
8- FOLLOWER AND SLIDE

9- OPERATING ROD

a- TRIGGER ... ...GER ...GROUP
c- HAMMER SPRING HOUSING

d- HAMMER SPRING
...ER SPRING ...GER
f- HAMMER PIN

g- HAMMER
h- SAFETY
i- TRI...

j- CLIP EJECTOR
k- TRIG...

10b- EXTRACTOR SPRING AND PLUNGER
10c- EJECTOR AND SPRING
10d
10e- BOLT
11- GAS CYLI... LOCK SCRE...
GAS-CY... LOC...

...-ELEVATING KNOB SCREW
c- ELEVATING KNOB
...UT LOCK ...ND SPRING
...- WINDAGE KNOB
g- APERTURE

...- COVER
(DISASSEMBLY
(SEE PAR 8 b (3) FM 23...
...PERVISIO...
...23- 5)

DISASSEMBLY AUTHORIZ...
...IATE SUPERVISION SE...

...BLY AND GAS...

How were those super-realistic charts done? The secret is revealed above in this picture taken at Springfield Armory. Ordnance photo technicians painstakingly mounted actual parts in position, then used a gigantic camera to make large high resolution photos. Artists would retouch the prints for clarity, emphasis, and to add explanatory notes.

FIELD STRIPPING   U.S. RIFLE, CAL. .30, M1

HOLD HERE
...ERT PRESSURE HERE
2

5 OPERATING ROD
6 BOLT
FRONT SIGHT
REAR SIGHT
BARREL AND RECEIVER GROUP
TRIGGER HOUSING ASSEMBLY
STOCK
DROP REAR END OF FIRING PIN IN BOLT AS INDICATED THEN SLIDE INTO BACK POSITION
HOLD BOLT HERE
Pull back trigger guard to unlatch ... then all the way down to disengage trigger housing assembly
OPERATING ROD SPRING
3 FOLLOWER ROD
OPERATING ROD CATCH ASSEMBLY
4 FOLLOWER ARM PIN
FOLLOWER ASSEMBLY
FOLLOWER ARM
BULLET GUIDE
Use numbers in circles for sequence of disassembly

ORD. No. 17987

BOLT AND GAS
U. S. R

AFTER BULLET PASSES GAS PORT THE PRE
ENTERS GAS CYLINDER AND ACTS AGAINS
PISTON-END OF OPERATING ROD. CAUSING IT TO

Even JOE DOPE can understand what goes where and why from these training aids. The main picture here is one of a series of flip charts on the M1. At left is a typically youthful lieutenant posing with the remarkable M24 oversized cutaway Garand. Below him, an NCO conducts a class using the M24 and easel-mounted flip charts. At the bottom, an infantryman demonstrates his speed at stripping and reassembly while blindfolded. How fast could **you** do it?

← RECOIL

RECOIL
LIMIT

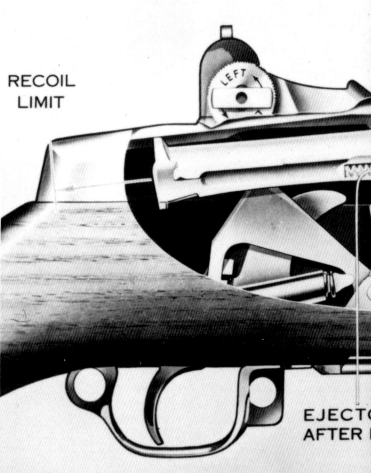

LEFT

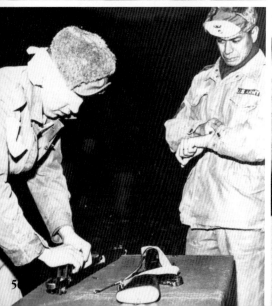

EJECTO
AFTER

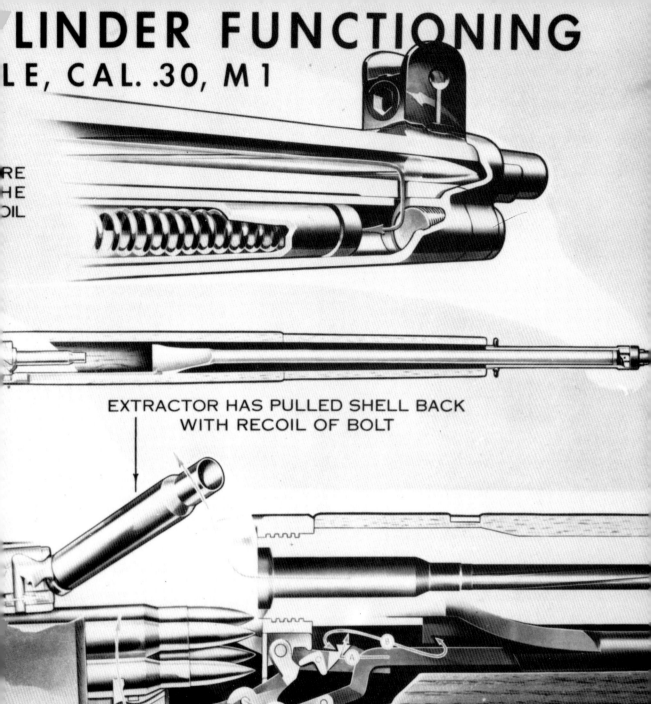

RE
HE
OIL

EXTRACTOR HAS PULLED SHELL BACK WITH RECOIL OF BOLT

AFTER THE LAST CARTRIDGE IS FIRED —
Ⓐ THE CLIP IS EJECTED.
Ⓑ THE BREECH IS LOCKED OPEN.

S SHOWN EJECTING SHELL
S CLEARED FIRING CHAMBER

ORD. No. 17989

By the Book...

FM 23–5

There's the right way, the wrong way, and the Army way. Field and technical manuals are portable fountains of knowledge showing the "Army Way" of doing just about anything. Used as directed, sergeants can teach, privates can learn, and everyone does it the same way. Just be careful, because loading according to FM23-5 of July '43 is absolutely certain to cause immediate "M1 Thumb"

WAR DEPARTMENT

BASIC FIELD MANUAL

U. S. RIFLE, CALIBER .30, M1

30 July 1943

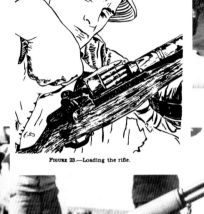

FIGURE 23.—Loading the rifle.

(20) **Enemy in Sight.**—Hold the rifle horizontally above the head with the arm or arms extended as if guarding the head.

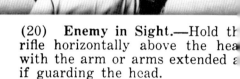

Cadence exercise.

Figure 63.—One-man fox hole with camouflage cover.

4 to 5 FEET
DEPENDING ON
HEIGHT OF MAN

FIRE PORT

ENTRANCE

FIRE STEP

SUMP

Shoot it, clean it, and then clean it again. As a matter of fact, you clean it even when it ain't been shot!

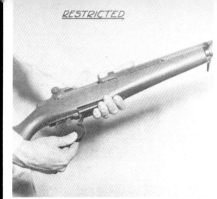

Manuals show how. The Mar '37 booklet had poor photos, but the Jul '43 version gave clear line drawings.

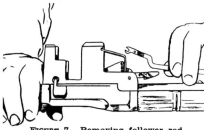

FIGURE 7.—Removing follower rod.

JoeDope is a regular ace
At 'cleaning' that rifle apace-
But the parts he gets sand on
With reckless abandon
Will jam and blow up in his face!

Don't be a dope! HANDLE EQUIPMENT RIGHT!

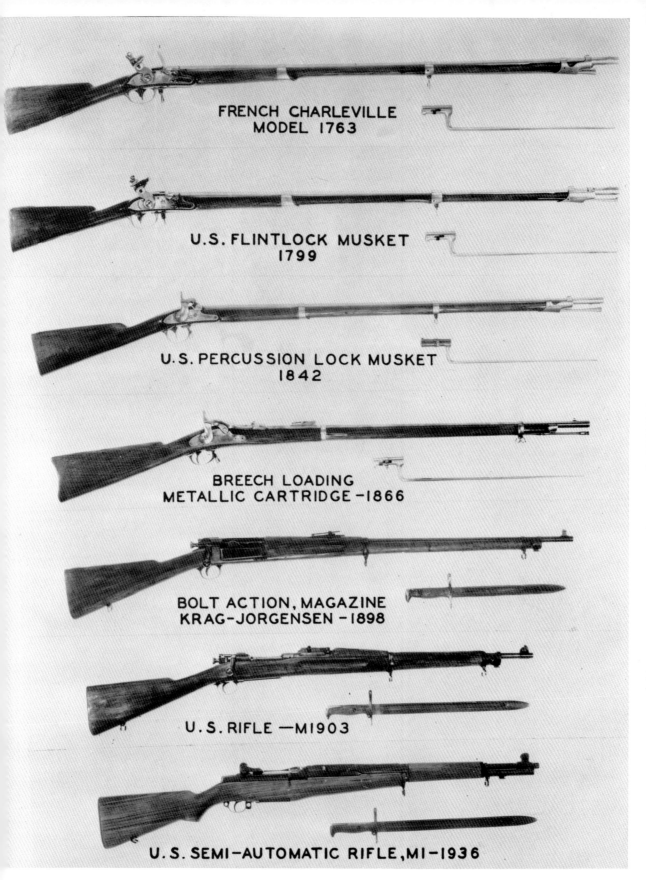

FRENCH CHARLEVILLE
MODEL 1763

U.S. FLINTLOCK MUSKET
1799

U.S. PERCUSSION LOCK MUSKET
1842

BREECH LOADING
METALLIC CARTRIDGE - 1866

BOLT ACTION, MAGAZINE
KRAG-JORGENSEN - 1898

U.S. RIFLE — M1903

U.S. SEMI-AUTOMATIC RIFLE, MI-1936

EPOCHAL TYPES

9 BACK TO THE BEGINNING

It was not until our involvement in World War I that the US Army began to seriously experiment with ways to increase the effective firepower of its foot soldiers. For various reasons the Browning Automatic Rifle, the "Pedersen Device", and other attempts were found wanting. Enter John Garand.

Sometime in 1917 it is said, National Guardsman Garand submitted drawings of a proposed light machine gun to the Army. This and follow up contact were apparently enough to result in his being hired away from the Bureau of Standards into the Experimental Department at Springfield Armory to work on the semiautomatic rifle program. His resulting T1920 (below right with 40 round magazine), was followed by the Models 1921, 22, and 24.

A thirty-something John Garand circa 1921-24 holds his primer-actuated .30 caliber second model rifle.

GARAND SEMI-AUTOMATIC RIFLE
DESIGNED BY JOHN C GARAND
EXPERIMENTAL DEPARTMENT
SPRINGFIELD ARMORY, MASS.

FARQUHAR-HILL RIFLE

SEMI-AUTOMATIC RIFLE
DESIGNED BY
SPRINGFIELD ARMORY 1918

SEMI-AUTOMATIC RIFLE
ROCK ISLAND TYPE

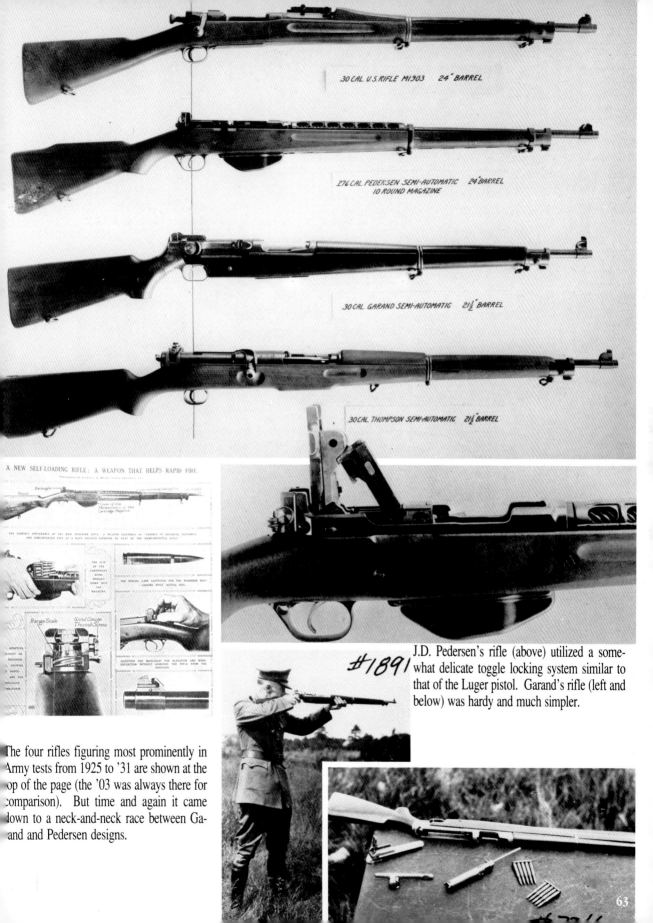

.30 CAL. U.S. RIFLE M1903   24" BARREL

.276 CAL. PEDERSEN SEMI-AUTOMATIC   24" BARREL
10 ROUND MAGAZINE

.30 CAL. GARAND SEMI-AUTOMATIC   21½" BARREL

.30 CAL. THOMPSON SEMI-AUTOMATIC   21½" BARREL

A NEW SELF-LOADING RIFLE: A WEAPON THAT HELPS RAPID FIRE

#1891

J.D. Pedersen's rifle (above) utilized a somewhat delicate toggle locking system similar to that of the Luger pistol. Garand's rifle (left and below) was hardy and much simpler.

The four rifles figuring most prominently in Army tests from 1925 to '31 are shown at the top of the page (the '03 was always there for comparison). But time and again it came down to a neck-and-neck race between Garand and Pedersen designs.

63

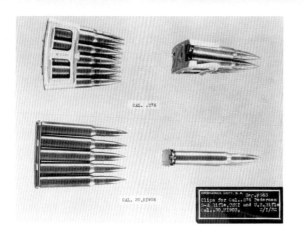

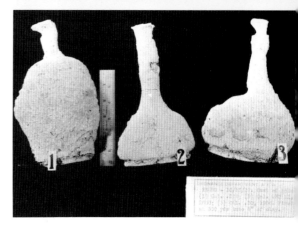

.30 Caliber vs. 7mm/.276

In the early 1920's Pedersen, who was a respected firearms designer also in the employ of Springfield Armory, induced the Army to make large quantities of a new 7mm cartridge for experimental purposes. This offered some compelling advantages over the standard .30-06 service round of the time, including reduced recoil, better ballistics, easier extraction, and lower per-round manufacturing cost.

It worked out well in both Pedersen's own rifle, and in Garand's new gas-operated T3 series. In fact, the .276 tested so favorably that the Army was preparing to standardize it in 1932 when Chief of Staff Douglas MacArthur stepped in with some well-considered objections. Caliber .30 would continue as the Army's main small arms cartridge for at least another 25 years.

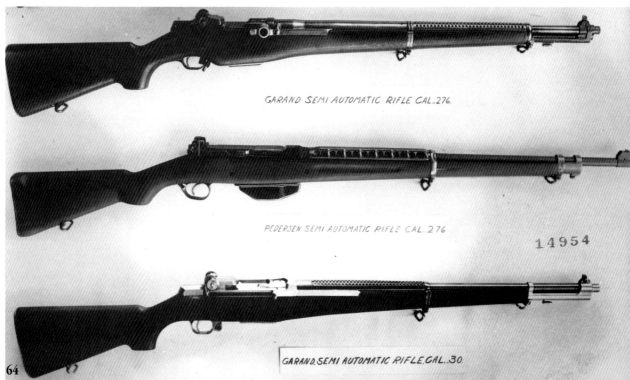

GARAND SEMI AUTOMATIC RIFLE CAL..276.

PEDERSEN SEMI AUTOMATIC RIFLE CAL..276.

14954

GARAND SEMI AUTOMATIC RIFLE.CAL..30.

Garand's .276 caliber T3 is for all practical purposes identical to the subsequent .30 caliber M1. It must have been a honey to shoot in reduced caliber; pumping out ten high velocity, low recoil rounds as fast as the trigger could be squeezed. Note the rounds counter on the left side of the receiver shown below.

No 8616 1 2 LUFKIN RULE CO 3 MADE IN U.S.A. 4 5 6 7

Garand Semi Automatic Rifle, Cal. 276, showing left side of receiver.

ORDNANCE DEPARTMENT, A.P.G.
27607 - 2/4/31.
Garand Cal. .276 Semi Auto.
Rifle T3 E2, #9. Left side.

CAL. .276, T3E2

CAL. .30, T1

ORDNANCE DEPARTMENT, A.P.G.
27822 - 5/4/31.
First Class, United States
Military Academy. At the
Small Arms Range.

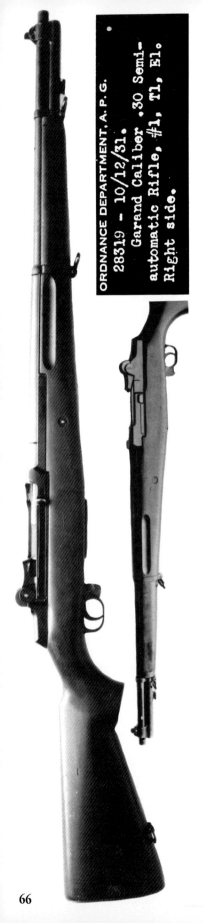

ORDNANCE DEPARTMENT, A. P. G.
28319 – 10/12/31.
Garand Caliber .30 Semi-
automatic Rifle, #1, T1, E1.
Right side.

When General MacArthur spiked the .276 cartridge, Garand needed to do little more than lengthen his rifle's receiver in order to accommodate standard .30 caliber service ammunition. His resulting T1 models successfully passed a series of tests at Aberdeen Proving Ground in 1932, leading to an order for a limited production run for 80 of the "US Semiautomatic Rifle, Caliber .30 T1E2". This designation was changed in mid-production to "US Semiautomatic Rifle, Caliber .30 M1". Thus, the birthday of the M1 is August 3rd, 1933.

U.S. Semiautomatic Rifle Cal.30 M1

Weight With Sling & Bayonet	Lbs. 10 - 8 Ozs.
Weight W/o Sling & Bayonet	Lbs. 8 -15 Ozs.
Overall Length of Rifle	Ins. 42.906
Type of Mechanism	Gas Operated
Feed	Clip En Block
Capacity of Clip	Rounds 8
Sight Radius (Battle)	Ins. 27.48
Sights Graduated To	Yards 1,300

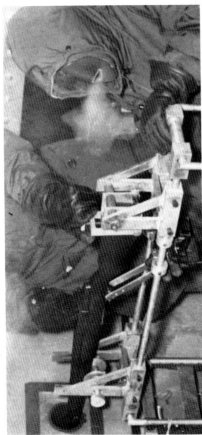

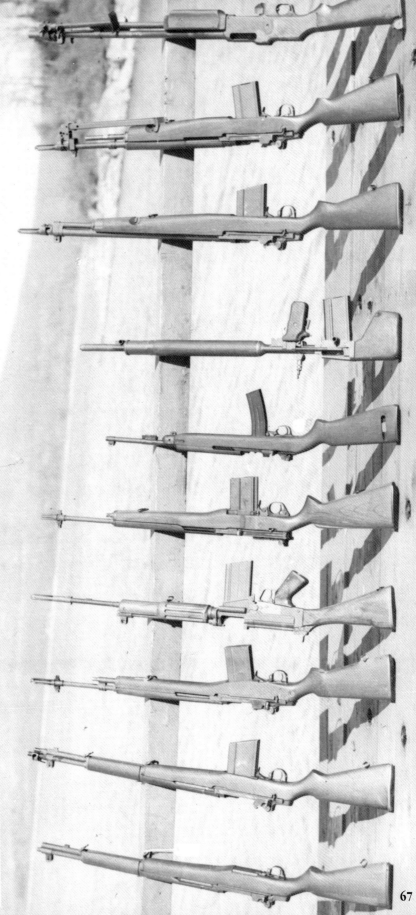

10 LET'S TRY THIS...

The urge to tinker is irresistible and development of the M1 did not slow by any means upon series production. Collectors delight in following the history of its modifications by observing both obvious external differences and more subtle ones charted by changing "drawing numbers" stamped into key parts. But what you're looking at here are some of many radical changes made by Garand and others in an effort to improve on near-perfection. One way or another these contributed ultimately to standardization of the "US Rifle, 7.62mm, M14" in 1957.

M1E5

Field Modification Similar to the T26 (M1 Carbine for comparison)

Garand's Selective-Fire T20

Bernard
Weiser's
Selective-
Fire M1

T20E1

T20E2

The first of Garand's T20 series of semi and full auto rifles were sent to Aberdeen Proving Ground for shakedown in November '44. Subsequent E1 and E2 variants endured many trials in various forms and calibers on the road to the M14.

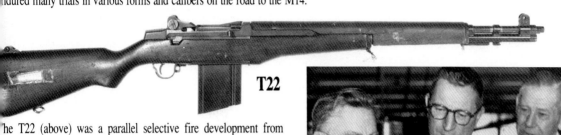

T22

The T22 (above) was a parallel selective fire development from Remington.

Garand (right) with his bullpup T31.

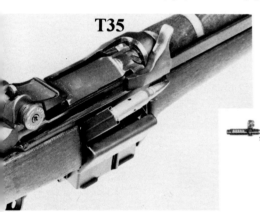

T35

CONFIDENTIAL

The T35 (above) featured a vertical cocking handle and Johnson-type rotary internal magazine.

7541-SA SPRINGFIELD ARMORY - ORDNANCE DEPT. 4 Jan. 1951
Rifle CAL. 30 T44 (T37 Incorporating gas cutoff and expansion
system.)

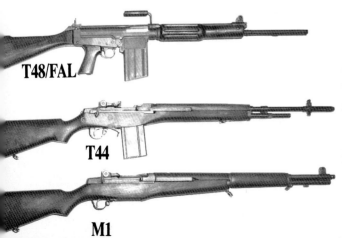

T48/FAL

T44

M1

T44E4/M14

11 GIMMICKS & GADGETS

This is sort of a catchall for some of the lesser known aspects of the Garand. After all, if you put a rifle in worldwide service for more than twenty years some unusual things are bound to happen. But, who would have thought of an over-and-under .30 caliber/37 millimeter?

Holes in your mitts are not as good as a squeeze bar in extreme cold.

"Takes a Licking... Keeps on Ticking!"

This unfortunate target dummy (above) is a casualty of the "Project Mercury" nuclear bomb tests of the 1950's. His M1 may be a little "hot", but probably will still work fine. The MULTILITE radioactive sights (right) are *purposely intended* to glow in the dark.

Look closely at this "1936" Garand. It's a 1/3 scale model just 37mm/14.5 inches long made entirely by hand by noted ordnance illustrator Andre Jandot in 1944. Where is it today?

12 WHAT GOES AROUND, COMES AROUND.

Over five million Garands were made in the US and abroad. During and after the Korean War, the M1 was adopted by many of the free world's armies. According to JANE'S *Infantry Weapons 1979-80*, the rifle was still in regular service with the armies of Chile, Costa Rica, Denmark, Greece, Guatemala, Haiti, Honduras, Italy, Philippines, Taiwan, Tunisia, and Turkey. Many other countries still had plenty on hand – bought, borrowed, or captured.

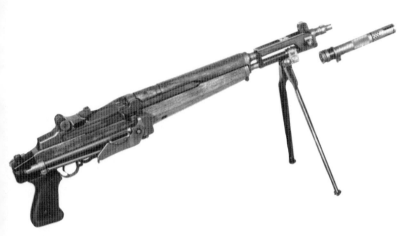

In order to help stimulate the local economy following WW2, the US set up M1 production with Beretta in Italy, where over 100,000 are said to have been built. Many of these were modified to 7.62mm NATO caliber or newly-made as the BM-59 (left).

A pile of Vietcong weapons captured by US Forces (below) includes this veteran Garand.

13 THE UNKINDEST CUT

Long after the M14 had eclipsed the M1 as America's "new" battle rifle, a trickle of Garands began to make their way into the hands of eager civilian high-power shooters. They were sold by the Army through the Director of Civilian Marksmanship (DCM) only to NRA members who could prove they were bonafide competitive shooters. Meanwhile, with obvious malice and apparent political motivation, faceless bureaucrats in the Department of Defense had quietly begun a massive "demilitarization" program on the 600,000 M1's classified as surplus. No matter that you may have carried an M1 in battle to defend freedom — you wouldn't be allowed to have one until it had been torch-cut into scrap!

The NRA blew the whistle on this disgusting episode with a powerful cover story in the February '78 AMERICAN RIFLEMAN. The storm of protest that immediately ensued is said to have eventually snuffed the cutting torches, but not before untold hundreds of thousands of "the best battle rifles of the century" had been destroyed.

American RIFLEMAN

FEBRUARY 1978

$1.50

YOUR TAXES AT WORK

(See page 12)

THE COVER: The United States Government's written policy now demands that money appropriated for national defense be spent to destroy usable military arms like this once functional M1 rifle. For details, see p. 12-14.

94th Year of Publication

M1 GARAND DEMIL RECEIVERS

Government cut rifle receivers. These have been cut between the l into 2 pieces. There is a gap where the cut was made and the ed of the rear half are jagged where they were chopped.

Garand Demil. **$14.95**/se

M1 "TANKER" GARAND
Short Barreled M1 (T-26), .30-06 or .308 cal.

SPRINGFIELD ARMORY™

Resurrection ...

Ah, but Americans are known for their ingenuity and some enterprising individuals set to reworking the scrap back into sturdy and fully serviceable rifles. In addition, a few companies like the civilian firm "Springfield Armory, Inc." made a name for themselves by rebuilding worn-out surplus to as-new condition for shooters and gun buffs. You can't keep a good Garand down...

But it wasn't until the late 1980's that federal import restrictions were relaxed to allow a veritable flood of Lend-Lease and Foreign Military Sales M1's back home again from Korea, South America, and elsewhere. Ranging from pristine collector grade rarities to rusted junkers, they all bear government-mandated stamping in the metal, forever branding them as returnees. But at least they're affordable and they're damn sure the real thing. Welcome home, boys!

M1 Garand Rifle
(With commercial mount & scope)

M1-D Garand Sniper Rifle
(Ultra-rare!)
(With M84 mount & scope)

SPRINGFIELD ARMORY, INC.

Photo caption format: **Date/Location/Description/Source**

When extensively citing official captions, exact wording will be in quotes. In the all-too-common instances where captioning information is incomplete or was not found with the images, the abbreviations (ND) no date; (NL) no location; or (NCI) no caption information; will be used. If it is very important for you to know more about a particular image, please write to the curator of the picture collection at the archive cited. Enclose a xerox copy of the whole page from this book on which the photo appears, along with a stamped self-addressed envelope.

With apologies to revisionist historians, guardians of the politically correct, members of certain nationalities, etc. **I have not censored** or otherwise altered the slang of the period. However, I have provided certain explanatory notes that I hope are at least fairly accurate and will be of value to a broad spectrum of readers. Please don't hesitate to write and let me know when I've missed the mark. This will be most valuable and appreciated for subsequent editions.

(ND) SA. John Garand holds a "1940" type M1. Officers unidentified. SANHS

Key to archives credited

AA	Army Art (US Army Center of Military History)		RBC	Robert Bruce Collection
LC	Library of Congress		SANHS	Springfield Armory National Historic Site
MHI	US Army Military History Institute		SMAH	Smithsonian Museum of American History
NARA	National Archives and Records Administration		USMA	United States Military Academy, West Point
NRA	National Rifle Association			Other sources will be credited with appropriate captions.

Cover and page 1, bottom right. 1945. US War Department official poster by artist Jes Wilhelm Schlaikjer. AA

Inside Front Cover, main. July 1944, Saint Lo, France. A patrol of the 29th "Blue and Gray" Infantry Division enters this hotly-contested city. NARA

Inset. 6 Dec 29, Springfield Armory, MA. 41 year old John Garand at the drawing table with his 7mm T3 rifle. SANHS

Page 1, top left. 2 May 57, Pentagon, Washington, D.C. The Army marked the passing of the torch from M1 to M14 (T44E4) with this publicity photo. SANHS

Top right. (NCI) Probably Springfield Armory, circa 1929-30. Garand's first gas-operated 7mm/.276 caliber T3 rifle. SANHS

Page 2. 9 May 1956, Ft. Belvoir, VA. NCO Academy students "Present Arms." NARA

Page 3. (NCI) Probably Springfield Armory, circa 1938. This is John Garand holding his "1936" model M1 in an alternate pose to the one used on the cover of *American Rifleman* magazine (see page 10). NRA

Page 4. main. Summer 1938, Ft. Hamilton, NY. Soldiers of the Army's 18th Infantry pose in gas masks and with bayonets fixed on their newly-issued Garand rifles. MHI

Top right. (NCI) Probably Springfield Armory circa 1937-38. Inspecting the muzzle end of a "1936" version M1. Note the early gas system. SANHS

Small inset. 1939, Ft. Bliss, TX. Horse cavalrymen with their new M1's in leather scabbards thunder up a hill. NARA

Pages 5-9. (NCI) Probably Ft. Benning, GA about 1937-38. As luck would have it, I found at the National Archives in the records of the Chief of Ordnance, the original photo prints used for production of the 1938 article in *Infantry Journal*. They are included here as they first appeared in the Sept-Oct issue. The crop marks and funny white outlines have been left on for effect. Somewhat more incredibly, VIRGINIA ENGRAVING -- the company that used to do IJ's photoengraving -- is still around. They were hired to shoot all the negatives for this book, which means this is the second time they've done these particular photos in a mere 53 years! What goes around, comes around. NARA

Page 10. 1938, Probably Springfield Armory. John Garand with his "1936" model M1, then entering accellerated series production at Springfield. NRA

Page 11, top and bottom. (NCI) Technical line drawings prepared by the Office of the Chief of Ordnance were supplied to the National Rifle Association (NRA), and other groups with military or firearms related publications. This particular set appeared in the Aug. '38 issue of *American Rifleman* with an article by Major G.H. Drewry entitled "Our New Service Rifle." NRA

Page 12, top. (NCI) Probably circa 1938 at Springfield Armory. Left side view of the "1936" first production model M1. NARA

2nd from top. (NCI) Probably circa 1938. Ordnance Department Technical Drawing. MHI

Middle. (NCI) Probably Springfield Armory circa 1936-38. "1936" version first-production M1 with M1905 bayonet fixed, and M1907 leather sling. NARA

Bottom. 1938, Springfield Armory. Ordnance Corps technical drawing showing a detailed parts breakdown of the first production M1. NARA

Page 13, top main. 1941, Puerto Rico maneuvers. Regular Army troops with the new "1940" model M1 featuring an improved gas system (see page 15). NARA

Top inset. April 1945. Field Manual (FM) 21-15, p. 73. "Method of Packing Individual Equipment on Horse." RBC

Bottom and right. 13 Aug 41, Ft. Benning, GA. Infantrymen model the new M1 helmet in a series of publicity photos. The new design gave significantly better protection due to improved design and use of special "Hadfield-manganese" steel. MHI

Page 14, main. 1943, Tool room of the experimental shop at Springfield Armory. John Garand shows how the 8 round *en bloc* clip is loaded. Note that he is almost using the proper technique of holding the cocking handle back with the knife edge of his hand, thereby avoiding the infamous "M1 Thumb." This is caused by allowing the thumb to be chambered along with the incoming cartridge, or when carelessly performing "Inspection Arms" in drill.

Inset. 25 Oct 38, Aberdeen Proving Ground, MD. A prototype version of the Johnson recoil-operated semiautomatic rifle as tested by the Army in 1938-39. Although innovative and well designed, it was not as good as the Garand. This was repeatedly borne out in subsequent Army and Marine Corps testing.

Page 15, top. July 1958, ROTCM 145-30, p. 33. Problems with the "1936" model such as heavy carbonization and sloppy alignment of front sight were corrected by redesigning the gas cylinder assembly in 1939. RBC

Top left. April 1942, Ft. Riley, KS. Chemical warfare training with the improved "1940" model M1. Office of War Information photo. LC

Middle. (NCI) Note the simplified M1 model web sling. MHI

Bottom. 30 July 43, FM 23-5, p. 3. RBC

Page 16, top left. 1942. War production poster by artist John Falter. Note the '36 style M1, and the old-type M1917A1 helmet.

(NOTE: most of the photos used on pages 16 through 18 are from a special series on Garand rifle production at Springfield Armory. Several were used in the Ordnance Department's June 1943 issue of *Firepower* magazine.

Right. 1943, Springfield Armory (SA). Paul Frodyma operates a twelve-spindle high speed reaming machine made by W.M. Steele Co. for barrel boring. NARA

Bottom left. 1943, SA Albert Circota checks M1 receivers after broaching. NARA

Bottom right. 1943, SA. Assembly Area Gangboss Joe Reynolds inspecting walnut stock blanks. NARA

Page 17, top left. 1943, SA. It takes only about six minutes to turn a stock blank on this automatic shaping machine. SANHS

Top right. (NCI) War production poster. NARA

Middle left. 1943, SA. Joe Reynolds again in the Inspection room after final assembly.

Middle right. 1943, SA. The stock undergoes final shaping

by hand prior to attaching its metal fittings. NARA

Bottom left. 1943, SA. Cleo Fleury checks clip loading function. NARA

Bottom right. 1943, SA. Using a sophisticated mirror device to adjust the sights on production line M1's saves time and ammunition. Art Tuttle says this guy's name is Kennedy.

Page 18, top left. 20 Sep 40, SA. Cartridge clip inspection. SANHS

Top right. (NCI) Among other things, Warner & Swasey made telescopic sights. NARA

Middle left. 18 Mar 44, SA. NARA

Bottom right. (NCI) SA. Packing Garand rifles for shipment. NARA

Page 19, top. 1943, Springfield Armory employees Alvis Hanson and Ray Chambers have an opportunity to put some of their handiwork into action as they get ready to fire a newly-made M1. NARA

Bottom. 29 Mar 43, Ft. Jackson, SC. S/SGT Loren Swisher issues a brand new M1 rifle to Private Francis Younkin. NARA

Inset. (NCI) War production poster. NARA

Page 20-21. 9 Sep 44, Belgium. "Yanks of the 60th Infantry Regiment advance into a Belgian town under the protection of a heavy tank." NARA

Page 20, inset. (NCI) "Mark Of A Man" by artist Nat White, portraying the Combat Infantryman's Badge and the man who earns it. AA

Page 21, inset. (ND) Sicily. Lieutenant General George S. Patton, Jr. with his leather and often mis-identified ivory handle revolvers (not pearl). The rifle in his jeep is probably a captured German Kar 98k. NARA

Page 22, top. 3 Oct 43, Guadalcanal. A display of "typical infantry weapons." SANHS

Middle. August 1942, Australia. Yanks pose with M1, .45 auto pistol, and .30 caliber Browning. NARA

Bottom. 22 Apr 44, Hollandia. Men of the 41st Division move inland against stiff resistance. Note the fired case in the air. MHI

Page 23, top. (NCI) A typical WW2 period Garand with M1 bayonet, M7 Grenade Launcher, and M9 High Explosive grenade. SANHS

Main photo. 1944, Leyte Island. "Three Jap snipers elected to shoot it out during the battle for Leyte. Yankee bullets drilled the Nips and dropped them in the muddy water of a bomb crater, where they sought shelter in a running rifle fight." NARA

Middle inset. (ND) 'Nhpum, Burma. "Corporal Bernard Martin of 5307th Composite Unit compares rifles with a Chinese ally." NARA

Left inset. (NCI) War Manpower Commission. NARA

Right inset. (NCI) US Army Official Poster. NARA

Page 24-25. (NCI) North Africa circa 1943. Layout of a "typical" paratrooper's gear -- possibly 505th Parachute Infantry Regiment. The M1 had to be broken down into its three main groups to fit in this early version of the padded "Griswold" jump bag. NARA

Inset. 24 Jun 41, Ft. Benning, GA. A demonstration of parachute infantry techniques. Note the A-2 cloth flyer's helmet.

Page 25, top inset. 4 Feb 43, Algiers. Soon after surrender, a former French collaborationist soldier tries out the M1. NARA

Bottom left. 14 Aug 42, Ft. Benning, GA. Staff Sergeant H.B. Hart sights his M1. NARA

Bottom right. 30Jul 43, FM 23-5. The bar-like "modified nut" was part of the fix provided by Ordnance to keep the rear sight from unscrewing and falling apart under rough handling. RBC

Page 26, top left. Feb 1945, Germany. A two man foxhole with a pair of begrimed GI's; one with an M1, the other with the equally famous Browning Automatic Rifle (BAR). NARA *Main.* Wartime cartoon by Sergeant Bill Mauldin, Stars & Stripes magazine European edition staff artist. Courtesy of Bill Mauldin.

Inset. Aug 44, Saipan. PFC Joe Vega, rifleman of the 27th Infantry Div. NARA

Page 27, top left. 19 Oct 44, Aachen, Germany. Private William Zukerbrow of Brooklyn pours it on the Krauts with his M1. Note the can of rifle lubricating oil tucked into his field jacket pocket. NARA

Top right. 24 Feb 45, Duren, Germany. 8th Division Private First Class Morton Fernberg of New Jersey, with a cigarette butt and an M1. NARA

Middle left. 27 Dec 44, Bastogne, Belgium. 4th Armored Division troops. NARA

Middle right. 29 Dec 44, Malmedy, Belgium. (Left to right): Sergeant Lyle Greene, Staff Sergeant Joseph DeMott, and Private First Class Fred Mozzoni take a break. NARA

Bottom. 15 Dec 44, Belgium. T4 Marvin Eans, Jr. of 1st Army shows off his new improvised snow camouflage. Note his bare right hand. There was no winter trigger kit at this time, and a gloved finger wouldn't fit inside the trigger guard of the M1. NARA

Page 28, Main. 9 Mar 45, Germany. Sergeant Claude Phelps of Baltimore, rifleman of the 94th Division, moves warily past a knocked-out Sherman and a pair of dead German machine gunners.

Insets. 30 Jul 43, FM 23-5. RBC

Bottom right, 30 Aug 44, Loriol, France. 7th Army Corporal Charles Hoff with a "good Nazi." NARA

Page 29, top. March 1945, St. Goar, Germany. "I drew an assault boat to cross in -- just my luck. We all tried to crawl under each other because the lead was flying around like hail." Crossing the Rhine under enemy fire. NARA

Bottom, main. April 1945, Germany. Linkup with the Russians on the Elbe River, as featured in *Yank* magazine. RBC

Inset. (NCI) Soviet infantryman with semiautomatic SVT-40 "Tokarev" rifle. The Tokarev was fairly common in the Red Army, but the bolt-action Mosin-Nagant was standard issue for Soviet infantrymen. Courtesy of Tom Nelson.

Page 30-31. 20 Feb 51, Korea. Infantrymen of the 17th Regimental Combat Team (RCT), 7th Infantry Division. NARA

Page 30, inset. July 1950, Korea. Private Jim Sullivan of the 24th Infantry Div. NARA

Page 31, inset. 10 Jan 51. Yoku, Korea. Private First Class Preston McKnight of the 24th Infantry Division. This native of New Cumberland, West Virginia is quoted as saying, "People are no damn good!"

Page 32, top left. 9 May 53, Camp Drake, Japan. Japanese laborers remove thick layers of Cosmoline preservative from M1 rifles stored since the end of WW2. NARA

Top right. (NCI) Korea. The strain of sustained combat is evident in the face of this exhausted GI. MHI

Middle. Feb 1951, Camp Cooke, CA. Spectacular pyrotechnics add realism to night training of these recruits in preparation for deployment to Korea. NARA

Bottom left. (NCI) Republic of Korea (RoK) Soldiers clean their M1's. MHI

Bottom right. 23 Mar 51, Ft. Ord, CA. Trainees on the range with M1's. NARA

Page 33. Back cover of the March 1943 issue of *American Rifleman* magazine. Note the "1936" type M1's. With just about all ammo and firearms production going to the war effort, Winchester/Western/Olin and most other manufacturers used advertising to inform the public and to build goodwill. NRA

Page 34, top right. 1955, Parris Island, SC. A Marine "Boot" gets *his* new rifle. "Grab it like a man, maggot!" NARA

Middle. May 1946, Parris Island, SC. Inspection Arms. NARA

Bottom left. (ND), Parris Island, SC. Probably early WW2. Marine recruits practice fire and maneuver under simulated chemical attack. NARA

Bottom right. 1955, Parris Island, SC. Recruits cleaning their M1's on long rows of tables specially designed for the task. NARA

Page 36, top left. (ND) Parris Island, SC. Probably circa 1950. "Three firing positions demonstrated by Private Will Richards of Amarillo, TX; Private John Eloff, Jr. of Gary, IN; and Private Harold Buck of Kansas City, MO." NARA

Top right. 12 Dec 56, Parris Island, SC. Using a carbide lamp to blacken the sights against glare prior to record firing. NARA

***Middle left.* 16 Apr 54, Ft. Benning, GA. NARA**

Middle right. (ND), Parris Island, SC. Sight picture instruction: "Battlesight zero is at 300 yards . . ." NARA

***Bottom.* March 1943, Camp Lejune, NC. LC**

Page 37, top left. November 1943, Tarawa. "They Weren't Fooling." NARA

(NOTE: Most of the pictures on pages 37, 38, and 43 are from a special exhibition of Marine combat cameramen's photos. Captions in quotes are the official titles of the pictures)

Top right. Nov '43, Tarawa. "Dead Jap." NARA

Middle left. Nov. '43, Tarawa. "Wounded Marine Proudly Exhibits Jap Sword." NARA

Middle right. Jul '44, Tinian. "Coming Ashore." NARA

Bottom left. Jul '44, Tinian. "Mopping up." Note the muzzle blast from the M1 in the foreground -- very rarely captured on film. NARA

Bottom right. Jul '44, Tinian. "Hide and Seek." The guy on the right has a .45 caliber M1911A1 auto pistol as the Marines root Jap soldiers out of their holes. NARA

Page 38, main. Feb '45, Iwo Jima. "From the crest of Mount Suribachi, the Stars and Stripes wave in triumph over Iwo Jima after US Marines had fought their way inch by inch up its steep lava-encrusted slopes." This photo was taken by Coast Guard Photographer's Mate Third Class John Papsun, not long after Joe Rosenthal's famous shot of the flag raising on the same spot. NARA

Top right. Feb '45, Iwo Jima. "The Foxhole Road to Tokyo." NARA

Middle Right. Feb 45. Iwo Jima. "Come out, Come out . . .NARA

Middle left. 1949. Roughneck Hollywood star John Wayne as Sergeant Stryker in "The Sands of Iwo Jima," one of the best movies ever made portraying Marines at war. RBC

Bottom left. Feb '45, Iwo Jima. "Radio Operator." NARA

Page 39, top row #1. (NCI) This is Amos Sewell's painting "Beach Assault," used for several different wartime posters. Scrap metal was important to the war effort. NARA

#2. (NCI) Hitler, Mussolini, and Hirohito are graphically skewered in this classic war production poster. War Memorial Museum of Virginia.

#3. (NCI) A very early, typically understated Marine recruiting poster. War Memorial Museum of Virginia.

Middle left. 1 Mar 43. *LIFE* magazine. US Steel Corporation's many member companies were justifiably proud of their prominent role in war production -- and the M1 rifle in particular. Courtesy of USX Corp.

Middle right. 1943. Tradition is important to the Marines, so each anniversary of the Corps is a big event -- particularly in wartime. NARA

Bottom row #1. (NCI) Every civilian could help finance the staggering cost of the World War by lending money to the government through War Bonds. NARA

#2. (NCI) Enemy spies used any available information to help predict the size, location, and date of allied troop movements and attacks. This Marine was shot in the face because some idiot's conversation was overheard. NARA

#3. (NCI) He's your boy, America! NARA

#4. (NCI) The message was often tailor-made for a particular audience. In this case, oilfield and refinery workers are urged to work harder in support of the island-hopping Marines. NARA

Page 40, top right. (ND) "The Rangers," by popular artist Mead Schaeffer. During the war, Schaeffer painted a series of *Saturday Evening Post* covers representing various services. AA

Middle left. (ND) A striking painting entitled "Infantry Under Fire," used in this spectacular poster urging quality in war production. Artist unknown. NARA

Bottom left. August 1942, Guadalcanal. GI artist Howard Brodie enlisted in 1942. He went on to cover war side by side with soldiers and marines in the Pacific and then Europe as a staff artist for *YANK* magazine. Brodie's front line documentary artwork earned him a Bronze Star. AA

***Bottom right.* (NCI) Artist Jes Schlaikjer's romanticized realism was powerful inspiration in a series of posters idealizing the men and women of the various branches of the Army in WWII. Vincent Leckey who retired in 1963 as a MSGT was the model for his Combat Engineer. Schlaikjer himself had served with the US 1st Div. in France during WWI.NARA**

Page 41, top row #1. (NCI) War workers, GI's, and the public could all help win by producing, fighting, and buying bonds. NARA

#2. (NCI) "Uncle Sam" with helmet and M1 urges GI's to take care of their weapons and equipment. NARA

#3. (NCI) Apparently, there was a problem getting GI's to take the threat of chemical warfare --and the usefulness of their gas masks -- seriously. NARA

Second row, #1. (NCI) Artist T.H. Jackson painted "The Infantryman" as a stirring tribute to the toughest job in the Army. AA

#2. (NCI) "G.I." started out as an abbreviation of "Government Issue." But it wasn't long before the American soldier adopted the initials for himself with wry humor. NARA

#3. (NCI) America's seemingly endless production of weapons and equipment must have led some GI's to carelessness and waste. NARA

Third row, #1. (NCI) Donations were needed also to support the good works of the American Red Cross wherever our boys--and girls--in uniform were stationed. NARA

#2. (NCI) Among other virtues, troops were also urged to be thrifty. NARA

#3. (NCI) Another of Jes Schlaikjer's infantrymen. This time he's caught under an enemy flare at night because somebody's loose talk tipped them off. NARA

#4. (NCI) Norman Rockwell, easily the best known and most popular artist of the time, painted this to honor the Army's riflemen who fought in key periods of American history -- now including WWII. AA

Bottom left. (NCI) After JOE DOPE, Eisner went on to become a staff artist at *MAD* magazine. The Army put his unique skills back to work during the Vietnam War with the famous "comic book" manual for the M16 rifle (DA Pamphlet 750-30, 1 Jul 69). NARA

Page 42, top left. (ND) WW2, Appenine Mountains. Signal Corps photographer Sergeant William McWerter with a typical Army issue Speed Graphic press camera. Its large 4x5 inch negative provided razor sharp grain free prints -- under favorable conditions. Problem was, each shot had to be laboriously made by inserting and removing a clumsy negative carrier. NARA

Top middle. (ND/NL) WW2. "Soldier with Pack and Rifle." NARA

Top right. 1944 (NL) Army maneuvers -- use of camouflage. The camo coveralls and helmet cover weren't popular in Europe because nobody wanted to be mistaken for a German sniper. NARA

Bottom right. 1950, Naktong Front, Korea. Corporal Carroll Vogles, squad leader of the 35th Regimental Combat Team. NARA

Left column #1. (ND) WW2, Aleutians. Cleaning weapons. NARA

#2. (ND) WW2, Ft. Benning, GA. Combat in Cities training. NARA

#3. September, 1951, Korea. Members of the Columbian Battalion of the 24th Infantry Division. NARA

#4. May 1945, Ft. Benning, GA. Staff Sergeant William Boyer in Officer Candidate Training. NARA

#5. October, 1945, (NL). Private Charles Cooper of Chambersburg, PA, sights his M1 sniper rifle. NARA

Center column #1. (ND) WW2, Ft. Benning, GA. Hand-to-Hand combat training. NARA

#2. (NCI) WW2, probably Colorado. Ski troop camouflage. Are his hands cold? NARA

#3. 1945 (NL), probably Colorado. Ski troops with Garands and an M1 Carbine. NARA

#4. (ND) WW2, Italy. *Nisei* (Japanese-American) soldier of the 100th Infantry. NARA

Page 43, top. Apr '45, Okinawa. "Life's Blood." With fixed bayonet jammed into the ground, a wounded Marine's M1 holds the transfusion bottle. NARA

Middle left. Apr 45, Okinawa. "Tanks for the Buggy Ride." NARA

Right. Apr '45, Okinawa. "Through 'Death Valley,'—one of the Marines of a Leatherneck company, driving through Japanese machine gun fire while crossing a draw, later called 'Death Valley' by the men, rises from cover for a quick dash forward to another position. The Marines sustained more than 125 casualties in eight hours while crossing this valley on Okinawa." A classic and well-known picture by Marine combat cameraman Bob Bailey. NARA

Bottom left. Apr '45, Okinawa. "One Man Paused." 6th Marine Division. It was common practice to mark the place where a brave man had died, using his rifle and helmet. NARA

Page 44, top left. 27 Sep 50, Seoul, Korea. An unidentified Marine rifleman squats in the rubble of South Korea's capital city. NARA

Top Right. 18 Sep 50, Korea. Warily advancing with fixed bayonet through North Korean emplacements. NARA

Middle left. 10 Sep 50, Pusan. Korean Marines with M1's. NARA

Middle right. 25 Sep 50, Seoul. Private First Class Albert Lumannis of the 1st Marine Division. NARA
Bottom left. 8 Jul 52, Korea. Sergeant Thomas Robinson of Roxbury, MA. Note his "flack jacket" body armor. NARA
Bottom right. (ND) Korea. Marines guard sullen Chinese Communist prisoners. NARA
Page 45, top. (ND) Korea. "Marine Winter Sporting Apparel -- Corporal Richard Griffin, left, of Torrington, WY, and Private First Class James Appleton, of Nashville, TN, compare the old and new outer uniforms worn on scout-sniper raids in Korea against the enemy. CPL Griffin is using the M1 with a *four power* (sic) sniperscope; while PFC Appleton has an '03 rifle with a sniperscope." NARA
Middle inset. (ND) Korea. Marine sniper.
Bottom. (ND) Korea. Sniper/spotter team of the 1st Marine Division. The issue 2.2 power scopes were barely adequate. Marine snipers are said to have strongly favored the '03 Springfield with its 4 power optics. NARA
Page 46. May '56, Ft. Ord, CA. Sergeant Paul Brockman of 10th Infantry with the T-1 Infrared Sight on M1 rifle. NARA
Page 47, top. 27 Aug 58, Ft. Benning, GA. Infrared Weapon Sight T-1, on what appears to be an M1C. Courtesy of *ARMY* magazine, Assn. of US Army.
Left. 9 Nov 44, Springfield Armory. Experimental flash hiders for M1. SANHS
Below. 30 Jan 45, Springfield Armory. M1C sniper rifle. SANHS
Bottom. 3 Oct 44, Springfield Armory. Griffin & Howe mount for M1C. SANHS
Page 48, top left. 18 Aug 50, Korea. 24th Inf. Div PFC Wilfred Stowe of Norfolk, VA. NRA
Main. 12 Aug 53, Ft. Sam Houston, TX. Reservists learn the capabilities of the M1D. NARA
Page 48-49, top. 30 Jan 45, Springfield Armory. M1D sniper rifle. SANHS
Middle left. 31 Jan 51, Han River, Korea. Sniper team of the 5th RCT. NARA
Middle right. 29 May 51, Korea. SFC Jack Moore of the 187th RCT sights his scoped M1 rifle. NARA
Bottom. (ND) Vietnam. Regional Forces Sniper with the M1D. NARA
Page 50, top left. (ND/NL) WWII. Lieutenant James Harden teaches bayonet fighting. LC
main. 13 Aug 41, Ft. Benning, GA. Publicity photo for the Army's new M1 helmet. MHI
Inset. 26 Oct 41, Camp Robinson, AR. Bayonet arch for a new bride and groom: Carolyn Cavender and LT Richard Belcher. NARA
Bottom left. (ND/NL), Phillipine soldier. LC
Page 50-51, bottom. Sep '42, Ft. Belvoir, VA. Bayonet practice. LC
Top left. 21 Apr 43, Ft. Jackson, SC. Bayonet practice. NARA
Below. (ND/NL) Probably circa 1950. Marine war dog handler PFC Lucian Vanasse with "King." NARA
Main. 30 Mar 51, Korea.
Below. 30 May 45, American Fork & Hoe Co. "Truing up blade of bayonet." NARA
Bottom right. 6 Aug 62, Springfield Armory. Inspecting M5A1 bayonet. SANHS
Page 52, main. 4 Dec 43, Ft. Benning, GA. NARA
Below left. (NCI) Rifle launched smoke grenade. NARA
Inset line drawings. Apr '49, FM 23-30. RBC
Page 53, top. 18 Jul 44, Lessay, France. The soldier on the left has just fired a rifle grenade at German positions. NARA
2nd row left. (NCI) Page from training chart on M1. MHI
2nd row on right. 20 Jul 54, Ft. Sill, OK. ROTC cadet. NARA
Bottom left. Jan '45, Germany. S/SGT Mel Scott of 29th Inf Div stands guard. The signal grenade on his launcher will be fired to alert the unit if an enemy is observed. NARA
Center. 14 Feb 45, Duren, Germany. Member of the 804th Ord Co. demonstrates wire laying techniques using a rifle grenade. NARA
Right. Apr '49, FM 23-30. RBC
Bottom center. (ND) Springfield Armory. Improved experimental grenade launchers for M1 rifle. SANHS

Page 54, top left. (NCI) WWII poster. NARA
Main. June '42, Ft. Benning, GA. CPT J.D. Butler with wooden mockup of the M1's action. NARA
Inset. 30 Jul 43, FM 23-5. RBC
Page 55, top. 14 Apr 54, Ft. Bliss, TX. Trainees strip M1's using cloth instruction mat as a guide. NARA
Bottom left. (NCI) Photo studio at Springfield Armory. SANHS
Bottom right. (NCI) Page from training chart on M1.
Page 56, top left. 25 May 53, (NL). 2LT Bruce Little with M24 training device. NARA
Below. 9 May 56, Ft. Belvoir, VA. SFC Paul McWilliams instucts students of NCO Leadership course. NARA
Bottom. Nov '57 (NL). SFC Elias Kaawakauo times a fellow "Blue Devil" of Co D, 504th PIR, 11th Abn Div. as he strips and reassembles an M1 while blindfolded. NARA
Page 56-57, (NCI) Page from training chart on M1. NARA
Page 58, top center and below. 30 Jul 43, FM 23-5. RBC
Top right. 18 Apr 50, Ft. Lewis, WA. Leaders course. NARA
Middle left. 12 Jan 43, Camp Butner, NC. CPL C.J. Jarr.
Middle right. Aug 1945, Drawing from MCS 3-26. RBC
Below. 1957, San Diego, CA. Former Marine Jack Webb produced, directed, and starred in the feature film "The DI." RBC
Below left. Jan '43, Ft. Belvoir, VA. PVT Paul Telline. LC
Page 59, top. 7 Jul 43, Newfoundland. T/5 Walter Barnett demonstrates picture perfect form with the M1 in a sitting position. NARA
Below. 15 Jul 53, Ft. Jackson, SC. CPL Doyle Wooldridge coaches PFC William Wheatley in the aiming box exercise. NARA
Drawings (except bottom right). 30 Jul 43, FM 23-5. RBC
Bottom right. Aug '45, MCS 3-26, RBC
Page 60, top left. (NCI) NARA.
Top center and right. SANHS
Middle left. 20 Jul 50, Korea. 1st Cavalry troops clean weapons. NARA
Center. (NCI) Will Eisner's JOE DOPE. NARA
Right. May '42 Convoy to Liberia. Negro troops clean their M1 rifles. MHI
Bottom left. 3 Dec 43, Goodenaugh Island. Armorer inspects M1 rifles. NARA
Bottom right. 6 Sep 51, Korea. PVT Jesse Cain, small arms repairman of the 707th Ord Maint Co. NARA
Page 61. (NCI) Circa 1938, probably at Springfield Armory. NARA
Page 62, top right. 1918, France. American doughboy at a listening post. NARA
Top left. (NCI) Model 1903 Springfield rifle, modified to accept a detachable 25 round magazine. NARA
Middle. (ND), SA. The top secret "Pedersen Device" of late WW1 was a blowback operated semiautomatic mechanism which replaced the bolt of the '03 rifle. Its low-powered .30 caliber cartridge was not considered effective and the whole idea was scrapped soon after the war. SANHS
Below left. (NCI) John Garand. NARA
Right. (NCI) Garand's Model 1920 semiautomatic rifle. SANHS
Bottom right. (NCI) Typical semiautomatic rifle designs of the WWI period were heavy, awkward, complicated affairs. NARA
Page 63, top. (NCI) Test rifles of the 1921-24 trials. NARA
Below left. (NCI) A clipping from and unidentified magazine article on the Pedersen rifle circa 1925. SANHS
Middle right. (NCI) Closeup of the receiver area of the Pedersen rifle. NARA
Bottom. (NCI) Testing the Model 1921-24 Garand rifle. NARA
Page 64, top left. 1 Feb 32, SA. "Clips for Cal. .276 Pedersen S-A rifle T2E1 and U.S. Rifle Cal. .30, M1903." SANHS
Top right. 13 Oct 27, Aberdeen Proving Ground, MD. "Cast of holes: (1) Cal. .276; (2) Cal. .30 M1, 2600; (3) Cal. .30, 1906. fired at 300 yards into 8" of clay." Looks to me like the .276/7mm Pedersen cartridge is a clear winner. NARA

Middle right. 24 Sep 30, Aberdeen Proving Ground, MD. "Cal. .276 Armor Piercing Bullets. 1. T1E1. 2. T2E1 NARA
Bottom. 10 Sep 30, SA. Comparison of Pedersen and Garand rifles. NARA
Page 65, top left. (NCI) An Army officer demonstrates the proper offhand shooting position for the new .276 caliber Garand T3 rifle. SANHS
Right. 13 Apr 29, SA. Detail of the T3 rifle's receiver. NARA
Below. 4 Feb 31, APG, MD. T3E2 rifle. NARA
Inset. 1 Mar 32, SA. "Clips for Garand rifle T3E2." SANHS
Bottom left. 4 Dec 31, SA. Garand receivers. SANHS
Right. 4 May 31, APG, MD. A West Point cadet tries out the T3E2. USMA
Page 66, top. 12 Oct 31, APG, MD. T1E1. NARA
Bottom. (NCI) The T1E2 in its initial production version. NARA
Right. (NCI) "U.S. SEMIAUTO RIFLE CAL. .30 M1" SN:5. The production version of the T1E2. Once the personal property of John Garand, this rifle is now in the collection of Garand Stand Report editor Billy Pyle. NARA
Page 67, top left. (NCI) Cold testing the M1 rifle at SA. Probably in the early 1950's leading up to the T44/M14. SANHS
Top right. (NCI) Using a high-speed time displacement drum film camera to analyze movement of the operating ro when firing. Probably in the early 1950's at SA. SANHS
Main. (NCI) Lineup of Garand variants and other experimental or production rifles and carbines. Quabbin Reservoir, near Springfield, in the mid-1950's. SANHS
Page 68, top right. 12 Feb 46, SA. John "Red" Stimson (left) and John Garand work on the flash hider for the snip version of the M1. SANHS
Left. 16 May 44, APG, MD. 18 in. barrel M1E5 with T6 pantograph type folding stock. Note attachment plate for the M15 grenade launcher sight. NRA
Below. 16 Sep 44, Brisbane Australia. A locally modified M1 with shortened barrel, gas system, and stock compared to a standard M1 carbine. The SA version of this was designated T26. NARA
Second from bottom. 7 Nov 44, SA. Garand's own selective-fire M1 was designated as the T20. NARA
Bottom. 2 Apr 46, SA. "View of M1 rifle modified for selective semi-auto and full auto fire. B.A.R. magazine in place. Muzzle brake and flash hider attached, and equipped with Bren gun bipod." This interesting bit of work is credited to one Bernard Weiser. SANHS
Page 69, top left. 5 Jul 45, SA. The selective-fire T20E1. Note the bipod and fan-like muzzle device. SANHS
Right. (NCI) Probably mid-1945 at SA. Detail of muzzle area of the selective -fire T20E2 with recoil check and bayonet attached. Its rate of fire was listed at 700 rpm. SANHS
Below left. (ND) SA. Remington Arms Co. delivered the T22 selective -fire rifle for tests at Aberdeen in Dec '44. SMAH
Middle of page, left. 3 Feb 54, SA. Identified on the back of the photo as the "T35." SANHS
Right. 17 Apr 62, SA. About nine years after retirement, John Garand visits the armory. The officer is unidentified, but the civilian with the bow tie is former German military small arms engineer Otto von Lossnitzer. SANHS
Below. 4 Jan 51, SA. T44. SANHS
Bottom left. (NCI) Probably circa 1955. NARA
Right. 13 Oct 55, SA. T44E4 -- eventually designated as the M14. SANHS
Page 70, top right. Nov '40, Ft. Oglethorpe, GA. 6th Cavalry troopers with motorcycle/sidecar rig and SCR-195 Radiophone. That's an M1 in the leather scabbard on the "iron horse." MHI
Below left. Jul '42, Ft. Sam Houston, TX. 37mm Antitank gun crew shows off an experimental spotting rifle - a barre mounted M1 rigged with a lanyard trigger and using explosive bullets. NARA
Right. Dec '43, (NL). Plastic protective "Invasion Bag" for the M1 rifle. MHI

MADE IN JAPAN, (NCI) A 1945 Japanese last-ditch copy of the Garand designated as the Type 5. It utilized the Type 99 7.7mm cartridge, loaded from two-5 round stripper clips into a fixed magazine. Less than 200 were reportedly manufactured. The Japanese also modified some captured Garands to fire 7.7mm ammo and issued them to naval infantry troops. SMAH

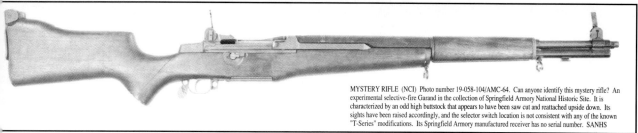

MYSTERY RIFLE (NCI) Photo number 19-058-104/AMC-64. Can anyone identify this mystery rifle? An experimental selective-fire Garand in the collection of Springfield Armory National Historic Site. It is characterized by an odd high buttstock that appears to have been saw cut and reattached upside down. Its sights have been raised accordingly, and the selector switch location is not consistent with any of the known "T-Series" modifications. Its Springfield Armory manufactured receiver has no serial number. SANHS

Middle of the page. 2 Mar 57, SA. This appears to be an experimental plastic or fiberglass stock. SANHS
Bottom left. (ND/NL) Probably during the Korean war. "Marine Sergeant Felix Saunders (left), of Los Angeles, puts to practical use the suggested invention of Sergeant John Polomsky, of Cleveland. The device permits rapid firing of the M1 and carbine during cold weather without the shooter removing his heavy gloves." NARA
Middle. (ND) "Colley-type winter triggers," on M1 (top), and M14. This kit also fit the B.A.R. SANHS
Page 70-71, bottom. 1942, Alaska. "Infantryman in Snow." Note his cutaway mitts. In extreme cold bare skin freezes instantly to exposed metal. Ouch! MHI
Page 71, top left. Jun '55, Ft. Carson, CO. CPT E. A. Treadwell communicates with PFC Elbert Croft on his new helmet radio. Gee whiz! NARA
Right. (ND) Camp Mercury, NV. Circa 1955. NARA
Below. (NCI) Multilite sights with radium dots. SANHS
Middle of the page, left. Circa 1972, Marietta, GA. Firing Max Atchisson's remarkable "Counter Recoiling Action Compensating Kick" (CRACK) modified M1 rifle. Photo by Don Thomas.
Below. 6 Apr 49, SA. Garand's own prototype T31 bullpup rifle fired the experimental short T65E1 cartridge. The cylindrical sleeve around the barrel is a novel pneumatic gas system. SANHS
Right. (ND) SA. "Prong type flash hider Drawing D7266434." SANHS
Left. 17 Feb 60, (NL). "Damage to cone type blank firing device caused by firing ball ammunition." SANHS
Bottom. 7 Dec 41, New York City. "1/3 scale model of U.S. M1 Garand Rifle. Made entirely by hand by Andre Jandot." Courtesy of Eric Ludvigsen, ARMY magazine.

Page 72, top right. 13 Nov 56, Germany. Soldiers of the Federal Republic learn to strip their M1's NARA
Middle of page, left. (ND) Korea. French army color guard. SANHS
Right. 10 Apr 51. Songjin, Korea. "Commandos of the 41st British Royal Marines plant demolition charges along railroad tracks of enemy supply line." NARA
Bottom left. (ND) Korean War. Turkish army PVT Capkin loads his M1. SANHS
Right. 5 May 52, Cambodia. Arms room for a unit of the Royal Cambodian Paratroops is filled with the US Foreign Military Assistance weapons. NARA
Page 73, top left. 1965, Dominican Republic. Honduran troops taking part in the US-led operation are fully armed and equipped by American aid. NARA
Right. (NCI) Thai Marines. NRA
Middle of the page. (ND) Italy. "BM 59 per paracadutisti." Beretta's 7.62mm NATO caliber selective-fire version of the M1 rifle as configured for paratroop operations. NRA
Bottom. (NCI) Vietnam War. Captured VC/NVA weapons. MHI
Page 74, main. Feb '78 AMERICAN RIFLEMAN magazine. NRA
Top right. Aug '53, Camp Perry, OH. CPT Harold Wheeler of Ft. Benning, GA, Mr. Charles Rodgers, of Pheonix, AZ. NARA
Below, middle and bottom. Circa 1955, SA. "Tons of guns -- all new -- all scrap -- Springfield Armory Bldg. 300, R & D Test Div. Area." Photo by Art Tuttle, courtesy of Billy Pyle, editor of GARAND STAND REPORT newsletter.
Inset. 10 Dec 91, SHOTGUN NEWS. Send $14.95 + $4 shipping to SARCO, 323 Union St., Stirling, NJ 07980 for

proof positive of the maliciousness that some government bureaucrats are capable of. By the way, SARCO's Glenn DeRuiter advises he was the one who supplied the demil M1 parts to AMERICAN RIFLEMAN for the infamous Feb '78 cover. Courtesy of SARCO.
Page 75, top and right. (ND) Springfield Armory, Inc. reportedly sold more than 9,500 newly built or refurbished M1 rifles, including the "tanker" T 26. Courtesy of Springfield Armory, Inc.
Middle of the page, left. 1 Nov 91, SHOTGUN NEWS. Springfield sporters is one of several firms offering recently returned M1's. Less than $250 is a great deal on a good shooter souvenir! Courtesy of Springfield Sporters, Inc., RD #1 (M1), Penn Run, PA 15765
Right. (ND) Camp Perry, OH. A Director of Civilian Marksmanship (DCM) Garand ejects its clip as the last round is fired during the annual National High Power Rifle Matches. NRA
Bottom right. 1991, Penn Run, PA. Re-imported M1's by the thousands are stacked on pallets in the warehouse of Springfield Sporters, Inc. Courtesy of Springfield Sporters, Inc.
Back cover, top. (NCI) WW2. "Clean Weapons Shoot Straight." NARA
Left. (NCI) WW2. "Joe Dope" never learns. Artist Will Eisner. NARA
Center. (NCI) WW2. "Mark Of A Man" -- the Combat Infantryman's Badge -- by artist Nat White. AA
Right. (ND/NL) Probably 1945. PVT Charles Cooper of Chambersburg, PA, with a sniper version of the M1. NARA

15 Thanks for the Memories

The following is by no means a complete listing of the great people who helped with this book:
Association of the US Army-Eric Ludvigsen
Carter Printing: Mike Lovins, Paula Barnes
Garand Collectors Association-Richard Deane, Scott Duff, Robert Seijas
Garand Stand Report- Billy Pyle, Art Tuttle
Institute for Research on Small Arms in International Security-Virginia Ezell
National Archives and Records Administration-Dale Connelly, Sharon Culley, Robert Ellis, Jonathan Heller, Nick Natanson, Holly Reed
National Museum of American History-Dr. Ed Ezell
National Rifle Assn.-Ron Keysor, William Parkerson III, Lourdes Fleckenstein
Kelsey Printing-E.L. Clevenger
O.F. Mossberg & Sons-Georgia Nichols
Olin Corporation-Jim Frigiola, John Falk
Presidio Press-Fran Nelson
Richmond Camera- Donna Toone and the Wild Bunch
SARCO-Glenn DeRuiter
Springfield Armory, Inc.-Vickie Lawrence
Springfield Armory National Historic Site-Barbara Higgins-Aubrey, Dru Bronson-Geoffroy, Stan Skarzynski, Don McTernan, John McCabe
Springfield Sporters, Inc.-Bill Rodgers
The Focus Group-Jorge Benitez, Lourdes Pogue
US Army Center of Military History (Army Art)-Marylou Gjernes, Joan Thomas
US Army Military History Institute-Michael Winey
US Military Academy-Robert Fisch
USX Corporation-Warren Hull
Virginia Engraving-Joe Schoppe
War Memorial Museum of Virginia-Bill Barker, John Quarstein
Warwick River Design -Wanda Cohen
Assistance, Support and Encouragement were also provided by: Patricia, Cristopher, Nicolas, and Matthew Bruce, LTC (Ret) & Mrs. Robert Bruce, Richard Newman, Jr., Bill Mauldin, Nelson Crockett, Tom Nelson, Thomas Cosgrove, "Little Joe" Cusumano, Blake Stevens, Jim Rose, Don Thomas, Carl Kindervater, Dick Chandler and the Notorious Chandler Gang. And lots of other people to whom I apologize for not citing by name.

(NCI) SA. THE ULTIMATE GARAND? The T20E2 Heavy Barrel model circa 1953. This .30 caliber selective fire weapon's performance compared favorably with the respected Browning Auto Rifle, and weighed a full four pounds less. SANHS

Bibliography

The following titles are readily available, not only from the publisher listed, but also from many firms dealing in military and gun books:

Hatcher, MG Julian S.
The Book Of The Garand
Gun Room, Press, 127 Raritan Ave. (M1)
Highland Park, NJ 08904

Duff, Scott A.
The M1 Rifle of World War II and *The M1 Garand: Post World War II*
Scott Duff, PO Box 414 (M1)
Export, PA 15632

Pyle, Billy
Ordnance Tools, Accessories, & Appendages of the M1 Rifle
G.S. Publications, PO Box 34005 (M1)
Houston, TX 77234

Mauldin, Bill
BILL MAULDIN'S ARMY
Presidio Press
31 Pamaron Way (M1)
Novato, CA 94947

Heller, Jonathan
War & Conflict: Selected Images from the National Archives 1765-1970
National Archives, Still Picture Branch
Washington, DC 20408

Stevens, R. Blake
US Rifle M14 from John Garand to the M21
Collector Grade Publications
PO Box 250 (M1), Station E
Toronto M6H 4E2, Canada

Canfield, Bruce N.
A Collector's Guide to the M1 Garand and the M1 Carbine
Andrew Mobray Publishers, PO Box 460 (M1)
Lincoln, RI 02865

Hoffschmidt, E.J.
KNOW YOUR M1 GARAND RIFLES
Blacksmith Corp., Box 1752 (M1)
Chino Valley, AZ 86323

PICTURES TELL THE STORY

Most gun books are filled with text and have a few pictures here and there. If you're like me, you want it the other way around. Why should you have to wade through somebody else's idea of what it's all about when you can see for yourself?

That's why I've started the WEAPONS IN PICTURES SERIES, jam-packed with hundreds of actual military archive images.

For the past several years I have been searching among the millions of pictures in the National Archives, Library of Congress, US Military History Institute, and other official collections. It has been a fascinating and exciting odyssy; uncovering thousands of photographs that precisely document the origin, development, manufacture, training, and battlefield use of American military small arms since the turn of the century. The majority of these wonderful old pictures have never been published, doomed to lie undiscovered and unappreciated by any but the most determined researchers.   Until now.

The book that you are holding is just the first of several in a planned series. Each will concentrate on one weapon or category of weapons that has served with honor in the hands of America's soldiers, marines, sailors, and airmen.

Upcoming books will feature:

Thompson Submachine Guns
Browning Automatic Rifles
The Carbine

"Ma Deuce" – Browning's .50 cal. Machine Guns
Bazookas and other Anti-tank Weapons
Odd, Unusual, and Obscure Experimentation
.30 Caliber Light and Heavy Machine Guns

Each will be in the same format and style as this, with hundreds of *real* pictures taken by skilled armory photo technicians, test documentation units, public information detachments, combat cameramen, and GI's themselves. And not just photographs, but also technical drawings, war art paintings, posters, cartoons, and training aid illustrations. Pictures tell the story!

Ask your military bookseller to be on the lookout for follow-on titles in the WEAPONS IN PICTURES SERIES

ROBERT BRUCE PHOTOGRAPHY
20th Century Land Warfare Archive Imagery

PO Box 482-M1
Sandston, VA 23150 USA